LIVING IN THE CITY

LIVING IN

THE CITY

AN URBAN RENAISSANCE

an exhibition of the international ideas competition organised by **THE ARCHITECTURE FOUNDATION**

Living in the City: An urban renaissance

an exhibition of the international ideas competition organised by
The Architecture Foundation

Exhibition launched at the Design Museum,
Shad Thames, London
1 February – 12 March 2000, with international touring thereafter

Exhibition Curator: Michael Weinstock, The Architecture Foundation
Project Co-ordinator: Susannah Woodgate, The Architecture Foundation
Project research: Kathryn Firth, Ingerid Helsing Almaas, Ia Hjärre
Exhibition Designer: Bentheim
Graphic design: Foundation Publishing

Catalogue edited by Michael Weinstock and Susannah Woodgate
for The Architecture Foundation
Designed by Jonathan Raimes for Foundation Publishing
Printed in Belgium by Snoeck Ducaju & Zone

Published by The Architecture Foundation,
30 Bury Street, London SW1Y 6AU
© The Architecture Foundation 2000

ISBN 0-9519067-2-0

Living in the City competition
and exhibition sponsor

Catalogue sponsors

The Living In The City project is supported by:
Corus, Railtrack, Capital and Provident Regeneration, Canary Wharf Ltd,
The Glass-House Trust, Peabody Trust, King's Fund, Berkeley Homes,
Manhattan Loft Corporation, Ove Arup & Partners, Evening Standard,
Byrne Bros Ltd, Hutchinson Whampoa, Schal International
and the Design Museum

The Architecture Foundation is revenue funded by the Commission for Architecture and the Built
Environment, Esmée Fairbairn Charitable Trust, Bovis and The Economist

CONTENTS

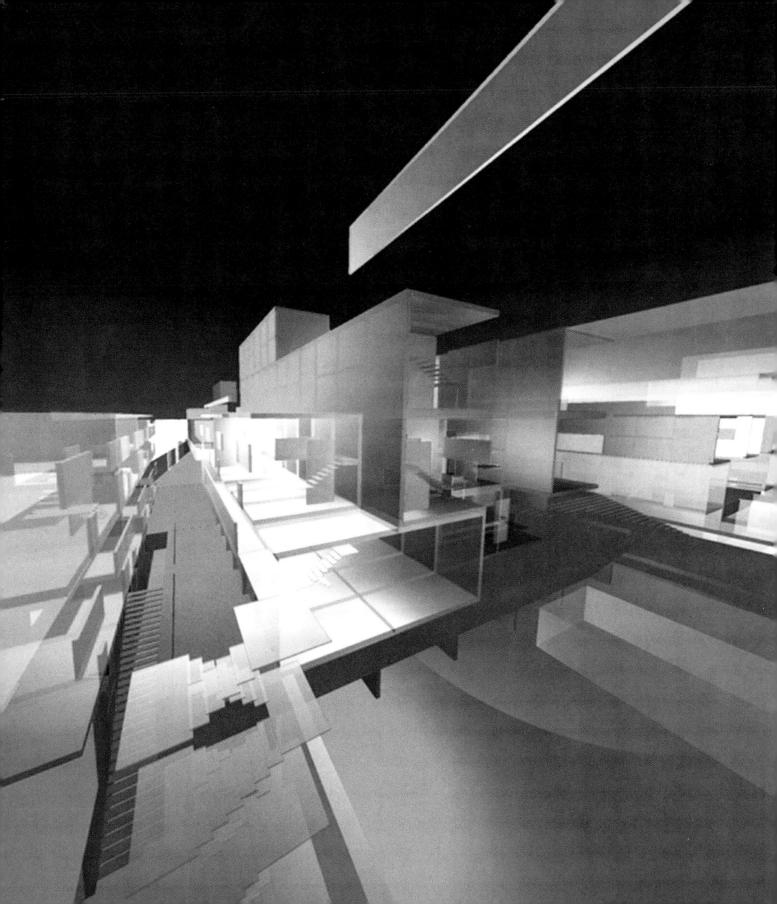

VISIONS OF THE FUTURE

If there is to be an urban renaissance, we need ideas and proposals about the city for public debate, landmark statements that will influence the future of our cities. British cities are at a turning point in their histories; and this generation has the opportunity of transforming them into some of the most habitable and civilised cities in the world. The aspiration to achieve a truly sustainable city for the next generation of urban inhabitants requires an inventiveness and exploration of ideas that the 'Living in The City' competition set out to provoke. It is an initiative that demonstrates the objectives and perspectives of the Urban Task Force, and the entries on show here research a range of issues associated with urban living and visions of the future city. The competition has generated a fascinating response, architects and designers from all over the world have entered proposals that show innovative ideas in sustainable and high quality urban design. I congratulate them for the great efforts they have gone to, and for the very high quality of their proposals.

London is a case study for the transformation of cities throughout the world. These proposals for the Bishopsgate Goods Yard, with their highly diverse mixture of programmes and mixed-income housing, are the forerunners of the sustainable high-density developments that will regenerate depressed and deprived areas of many cities. Environmentally sensitive strategies for design are needed for this task, and the innovative construction ideas and material uses that are explored by the competitors are extremely useful to provoke a dialogue with planners, developers and other decision makers. Reducing urban consumption, waste and pollution is central to combating environmental crisis and provides the basis for a healthy and urbane quality of life.

We must build cities for flexibility and openness, working with, and not against, the now inevitable process whereby cities are subject to constant change. The permeability of the site to the public, higher densities and multiple connections are essential part of the overall strategy to entice people back into the city.

Lord Rogers of Riverside

THE COMPETITION

The Architecture Foundation and Living in the City

In May 1999 an invitation went out from the Architecture Foundation to architects throughout the world to take part in an open ideas competition for the future of urban living. The brief called for ideas about housing in a sustainable high density project located on a large brownfield site, Bishopsgate Goods Yard in Spitalfields. Although the competition site is located in London, the intensification of urban living and the regeneration of derelict sites is an issue for all major cities the world over and this competition provides an opportunity to develop models of urban accommodation that will have a far reaching impact.

The brief called for innovative projects which incorporate a mix of tenures and uses and address the issues of social and environmental sustainability. This follows from the Architecture Foundation's commitment to the idea that high density mixed tenure housing is the most effective way to revitalise our cities, being environmentally, socially and economically positive. As there are very few built examples, this competition will help define future models.

The Architecture Foundation is an organisation established to promote high quality contemporary architecture and urban design to as wide an audience as possible. The Foundation has a number of specific objectives with which it seeks to achieve this aim:

• to promote the debate on the design, planning and welfare of our cities
• to develop local and national strategies for urban environmental education and participation
• to encourage the recognition of young architects and designers, and celebrate the work of more established practices

The Architecture Foundation's work, through demonstration projects is unique in that it cross cuts environmental and social issues bringing together high quality urban design input and innovation in public participation to foster urban renaissance in Britain.

The Foundation has developed a number of initiatives in the last three years that deal with many different aspects and scales of urban design and regeneration. These include:-

'Future Southwark' – a model 'petit project' of national significance, showing the Foundation's commitment to process and younger practitioners, which heralded Southwark's pioneering urban regeneration programme. Four projects are now built or underway.

'London interactive' – the first ever public resource of digital information on contemporary architecture in London and further urban developments; four 'layers' exist: buildings of the past 10 years, projects for the next 10 years, transport infrastructure present & future, and the work of the Foundation.

'The Roadshow' – a pioneering exercise in public participation which has toured the London Boroughs at the invitation of Local Authorities. The Foundation acted as an independent broker staging four-month programmes of public events, street festivals, education programmes and design group meetings resulting in proposals which the Local Authorities committed to implementing. The Roadshow was initiated to test and develop a model to be offered nationally. Since the Roadshow was first launched in February 1998 it has facilitated projects on 18 sites throughout three London Boroughs. Over £4m has already been found for these derelict sites.

'Car-free London' – a year-long public campaign to enlist wide public and professional support for new ideas to improve transport and public space issues. Over 200 ideas from public, students and professionals generated a massive media coverage. Acknowledged and endorsed by ministers and mayoral candidates as an effective, fun and creative catalytic project.

'School Works' – a project designed to explore how improvements in secondary school buildings might enhance academic achievement. The School Works project seeks to raise a national debate through the re-design and refurbishment of a secondary school in inner London. Architects chosen through a competition will work with pupils, staff and the wider community in an intensive participatory exercise to develop a brief. The participatory process and ensuing capital works will be funded by DfEE, which supports School Works as a unique project of national relevance, with the potential to change the way in which school buildings are procured, designed and managed. A pamphlet outlining the School Works approach has been circulated to all secondary schools in England.

The 'Living in the City' Competition

The first stage of the competition had 88 submitted designs and, of these, 6 were selected to develop their ideas further:

B Consultants

Bryant Priest Newman

Cartwright Pickard

Arthur Collin Architect

Bill Dunster Architects

Group for Architecture

and to join the teams who had been invited to submit designs for Stage 2:

Alsop and Störmer

Hamzah Yeang

Horden Cherry Lee

Renzo Piano

Helmut Richter

Ian Ritchie

West 8

Special mentions were made for the entries from Ash Sakula, Imago Architects, Gino Griffiths Architects, Morpheus and student Jason King, awarded the Evening Standard (Homes and Property) £1000 student prize. Following the launch of the Design Museum exhibition in January 2000, Peabody Trust and Manhattan Loft Corporation will award commissions to two of the design teams.

Jurors: Richard Rogers, Chair of the Architecture Foundation and the Urban Task Force; Herbert Girardet, Footprint Films; Piers Gough, CZWG Architects; Harry Handelsman, Manhattan Loft Corporation; Geoff Hooker, Corus; Sir Robert Horton, Railtrack; Helene Jourda, Jourda Architectes; Rabbi Julia Neuberger, King's Fund and Dickon Robinson, Peabody Trust.

Jury Advisors: Sustainability - Professor Brian Edwards, University of Huddersfield; Housing - Michael Weinstock, Architectural Association; Engineering - Tony Fitzpatrick & Rob Kinch, Ove Arup & Partners.

The Architecture Foundation would like to thank all those people who have worked so hard and given so much support to this important public project.

FOREWORD

The population of central London is on the rise again for the first time since the decline precipitated by the Second World War. Europe's largest city is booming. A potent combination of financial and media services, a vibrant and increasingly broadly based artistic and cultural environment, a large and expanding academic and research nexus of universities, hospitals and learned institutions. Europe's largest and most varied community of professionals are interacting dynamically to reveal the drivers behind the reshaping of major cities in the coming century. London's new found sense of confidence and energy has resulted in, or perhaps been stimulated by, a massive influx of new residents from all over the World. Already half of all of the minority ethnic citizens of the UK reside in London and it is perhaps this feature of London life which more than anything else gives credence to its claim to be Europe's World city. And thus it has always been. Key figures in London's financial, artistic and even political life have frequently originated from abroad, moving to London to escape persecution or to make their fortune or both. London's continuing success demands that this cycle continues. And so it does with an army of foreign financiers matched by a massive influx of destitute asylum seekers.

Although London has traditionally exhibited a particular magnetism all cities possess this appeal to a greater or lesser extent. Now in the era of electronically integrated global economic activity, continuing international strife and the relentless growth of the World's population, major cities will continue to be the key growth nodes. Particularly those which achieve a critical mass in size, economic significance, relative political stability, an essential sense of multi-cultural representation and tolerance, and accessibility to new populations.

The combination of the flow of these new populations into London along with the emerging trend of a return to urban living, especially by childless households, young and old, is exerting massive pressure on the housing market. House prices have risen rapidly over the past few years in reaction to demand from those well paid in the London economy and those investing from abroad. This has resulted in a widening gap between those who can and those who cannot afford to own their home. As a consequence fewer council and housing association tenants are leaving to purchase their own homes and this reduction in turnover coupled to the depletion of the stock of social housing resulting from right to buy sales, has caused a record increase in the number of homeless families currently accommodated in temporary accommodation. The commercial development industry has responded energetically to rising demand, and central London has seen an unprecedented building boom in new apartment blocks, and the conversation of redundant offices, hospitals and civic buildings. Originating in Docklands this phenomena has spread up the Thames and around the City creating a new market for apartment and loft living. The new metropolitan lifestyle has become firmly established. However while the affluent are happy and able to pay premium prices for high-rise, high density living in urban environments such as the Barbican, Bankside, Chelsea Harbour and even the Thames Barrier in Docklands, the majority of the British public still tends to equate high-rise and high density housing with the perceived failure of post-war local authority housing estates. Perhaps as a consequence much of this new housing is being bought up by investors for rental to the transient international community.

Meanwhile high land values make it increasingly difficult for housing associations to purchase sites and buildings for their client groups. As a result they are increasingly dependent on Section 106 planning deals which are intended to allow for up to 25% of new housing developments to be affordable. But it is increasingly clear that the latter mechanism is an inadequate device to provide London with the amount of affordable housing which it requires both to deal responsibly with homelessness and to enable the economy to continue to operate effectively. While concerns for homeless families and asylum seekers are well established it is now recognised that with current levels of public investment only the most needy can expect to get access to social housing. There is therefore rising awareness of the need to provide appropriate housing for the hundreds of thousands of economically active but low paid employees in the London economy. Many of these are young people emerging from tertiary education to provide much of the entrepreneurial creativity and drive which a successful city requires. Putting the economy first suggests that their housing needs should be taken just as seriously as those of others.

As a charity for poor Londoners, the Peabody Trust is worried that London's increasing prosperity appears to be accompanied by an actual increase in the number of citizens experiencing real poverty. This phenomenon is also shown by other cities and represents the biggest long-term challenge to the urban dream. It is critical that the supply of high quality affordable housing of all types keeps pace with increasing populations. It is also critical that stocks of inexpensive and affordable housing are managed and maintained in a manner appreciated by all sectors of society so that confidence in our cities is sustained and urban flight avoided. Rather than repeat the massive estates of mono-cultural housing of the middle years of this century we need to develop more naturally mixed communities where all residents can exercise greater choice. Choice over where they live, what they live in and how they live. Critically our new urban environments must be sufficiently attractive to ensure that the urban model increases its appeal to as many people as possible.

The backdrop to this scene is the debate about where Britain's growing population should be housed and in particular in the south-east where the pressure is greatest. Everyone seems to agree that previously used land should be prioritised for development so as to reduce the pressure to develop virgin countryside. However there is little agreement as to the practicality of this strategy nor how many people can be accommodated in London and other towns and cities. So far the Urban Task Force report has had little impact on local authority planning departments, or public perception. Planning applications are still assessed against Local Authority UDP policies with their outdated densities and parking standards. As a result there are relatively few models in this country of successful higher density, mixed-use urban environments. While it is recognised that say the centre of Paris has densities far higher than London, and that high-rise living is regarded the norm in say Singapore, these are generally not thought relevant or appropriate to London with its extensive conservation areas, or other British cities. And yet with London and indeed the UK's other major cities becoming increasingly multi-cultural it seems that a much more energetic exploration is needed of new urban residential forms, which can respond to the global urbanisation of the developing world and to the evolving e-cultures of the developed world. Living in the City has been designed to be a springboard for just such a debate. The goal we have set has been to bring together current concepts of sustainability, urbanity, multi-culturalism, and social inclusion by challenging established planning concepts such as density, land use and car based transport planning, within an overall architectural challenge to provide high quality environments at reasonable cost and in an aesthetic language that can delight, excite and enthuse the widest possible sector of society.

Dickon Robinson
Peabody Trust

HEALTH AND WELL-BEING

The King's Fund welcomes the opportunity to contribute to this important event. We see the health agenda as being inextricably linked with the regeneration of our cities and we await the outcomes of this competition with great interest.

We start from the premise that, important though the sensitive physical development of any brownfield site undoubtedly is, it must be related to the regeneration of the wider environment in social and economic as well as physical terms. Just as the brief correctly identifies the importance of land use and social mix within the site, so issues must also be addressed beyond its boundaries if we are to avoid the emergence of a privileged island in a sea of comparative deprivation.

The contribution that follows is based on a paper commissioned from Professor Drew Stevenson of the University of East London by the King's Fund for a conference last October. It explores the relationship between health, regeneration and the development of brownfield sites as well as the wider issue of well-being in urban society.

Anna Coote, Director
Public Health Programme, King's Fund.

This competition is about doing things in new and imaginative ways. When considering the future, we need some sort of context in which to place policies – and to understand constraints. Trends tell us more about the past than the future, but a growing body of work now makes it possible to frame a view of the future – barring global catastrophes. I want to look briefly at two contextual changes – in societal relationships and in values – because they seem to me to be central to understanding what demands people will make on urban living.

A marked change has swept powerfully across the UK and the developed world in the past 40 years. This has been described as a shift in relationships from a model of dependence (based in the post-war welfare state), to a model of independence (based in the Thatcher years) to an emergent model of interdependence. Consider, for example, the concept of stakeholding, the creation of 'just in time' delivery models, or the current emphasis on partnerships: these new ways of working are not a product of coincidence or fashion, but reflect deep-seated changes running through society. They are likely to intensify and have fundamental implications for the effective delivery of key policies - including regeneration, development and health.

These changes are mirrored at the individual level by the breakdown of certain rules of organisation and control. Within the past ten years or so we have witnessed a steep decline in people's trust in institutions and in authority and a complete loss of deference as a way of ordering society. We are seeing the birth of a society that is less easy to order, less compliant and more questioning; a society where people want less control by others over their lives – even though the media may be reproducing new forms of control, through its power over information and 'style'.

This is part of a gradual but deep-seated shift in values. Longitudinal surveys in the UK have shown that people tend to form their values between 17 and 24 and then carry them throughout life, changing only

IN CITY LIVING

at the margins. Significant changes occur over time because of different values held by succeeding generations. There has been a long-term shift away from values associated with the post-war need for shelter, stability and survival and the consequent need for authority and external control, towards values based more on integration, emotion, ease and green issues. These changes largely transcend gender, race and class. They will continue to transform lifestyles, ideas and expectations – as well as notions about relevant policy making in the future.

The move towards greater interdependence, coupled with the emergence of an ageing population and a generation that is less likely to accept imposed solutions, is likely to have profound effects for the future delivery of health improvement, as well as on the sustainable development of brownfield sites.

It cannot be assumed that attractive, innovative and lively environments will in themselves keep people, even 'advantaged' people, living in the city. The bottom line for a new generation that has choice will be their expectations for a good quality of life, including health, and for real control over their local community. So the development of large sites in future will need to take the health agenda more explicitly into account. This is because health is already a huge 'growth industry' and there are expectations that improvements in health should, and will continue. But the concern is much more deep-rooted.

We are entering an age where, for UK society as a whole, the basic elements of survival – food, shelter, safety from attack – feel more firmly secured than in the past. Consequently, people are less preoccupied with struggling to survive and more interested in promoting their chances of a long and healthy life. The attempt to create a new world order in which global war does not threaten extinction; growing concern over other potential catastrophes (global warming as well as local 'green' issues such as pollution); opposition to hidden dangers in what we eat (BSE, GM foods and the promotion of organic crops) and a new focus

on personal health (through fitness clubs, for instance): all these are examples of people trying to take control over matters they see as influencing their life chances. It is unlikely that the instinct driving this will change; it may emerge in new forms, but health will stay at the top of the agenda.

How do health and regeneration interact? It is no coincidence that regeneration policies and actions are designed to influence the whole range of issues that combine to produce health or ill health in individuals during their lifetime. They are targeted at individual lifestyle, social and community influences, living and working conditions and wider social, economic, cultural and environmental conditions. They are also increasingly targeted at the discrimination faced by black and ethnic minority communities which leads to social and economic exclusion and poorer health. If regeneration policies succeed in tackling some or all of these issues, then it follows that health will improve – unless of course all accepted wisdom regarding the factors producing health are wrong.

Similarly, issues of power and control over one's own life or local circumstances are increasingly recognised both as essential to sustainable regeneration and as important determinants of health. Also, like health, regeneration has no end-state: it is relative and expandable.

A central question must be how to improve the integration of regeneration and health policy (not just how regeneration might promote health, but also how health might work more holistically with regeneration partnerships). Is it possible to envisage a different kind of health provision in localities, including large brownfield sites, to secure a better quality of life?

Regeneration policies are already targeted at areas of deprivation. Those areas mostly display greater problems of ill health and poorer local provision of health services. Capital money could be targeted on the provision on a new generation of integrated healthcare/well being centres in the most accessible and central locations for those communities. Interactive technology could be installed to provide links to local/regional hospitals and to centres of specialist support. Such links already exist in the USA, for purposes ranging from distance learning for health professionals to virtual consultations between patients and clinicians. Equally important, these centres could have links with libraries, schools, housing offices and community centres to encourage access to health support from different environments. And they could act as crisis centres offering non-stigmatising support for people at risk of mental illness.

Regeneration funding could also be channelled into health-related housing initiatives, such as supported accommodation for Black elders, or Foyers offering help to young people with mental health problems. More radically, there is potential to train local people to engage in health care as a way of building up appropriate services run by local people. This would de-mystify and de-professionalise health services while ìbuilding the capacityî of local people. It would also strengthen local networking, making it easier to identify those who are in need of support, since many of the most vulnerable groups do not come forward through more formal processes.

Many brownfield sites, particularly in Greater London, lie within or adjacent to areas of deprivation – and hence, as we have seen, adjacent also to areas of poor health and poor health services. Large brownfield sites therefore present a real opportunity to address issues of social exclusion, of capacity building and of improved health in the surrounding areas. They also represent significant opportunities to reflect and enhance the diversity of different local communities.

How could all this be achieved? First, sites should be designed to be open to the surrounding communities and to be an outward looking resource, rather than an inward looking fortress. Large sites cannot be seen in isolation – they are an essential a resource in the regeneration toolbox. Planners need to analyse what is lacking in the social and community fabric of the surrounding area and ensure that as much as possible is provided on the site. Examples of provision will vary from site to site, but may include social housing and open space, as well as a range of social facilities such as education, one stop shops for local services, and integrated health centres, as described above. These should be assessed carefully and regarded not as negotiable planning gain to be added on, but as reasonable requirements for site development, without which planning permission would not be granted.

Second, there are non-physical assets that could be provided or located on such sites. For example localised training schemes, such as those provided in the Foyer movement, could be offered for all residents - ranging from life skills, to employment skills, to lifelong learning with careers advice and job placement services. There could be a Section 106 (planning gain) fund set up to improve the social and community facilities of the surrounding areas, managed by a local Development Trust (the Paddington Regeneration Partnership provides an example). And in all these possibilities the maximum opportunity should be taken to build the skills and capacity of local people – not just so that jobs are created by the development, but also to increase employment in town centres and to promote local management and control of local services and facilities. A strong sense of local ownership is an essential pre-requisite of sustainable regeneration and of building a community that moves towards a greater sense of well-being.

Whatever practical problems are set against the opportunities (and of course these will vary site to site), one thing is constant. Those involved in developing larger brownfield sites must make it a priority to reach out and impact positively upon the wider community. If they don't, then it is not simply an opportunity foregone. As always in an unequal society anything that maintains the status quo, rather than challenging and changing it, becomes part of the problem.

What, ultimately, can we hope to achieve? From a health perspective, the challenge is to imagine a society that has largely conquered ill-health, promoted active good health in a physical sense and started to transcend even that – which takes us into uncharted waters.

Arguably, we might arrive at a point where people did not think the grass was always greener on the other side, where there was a sense that enough is enough rather than a fixation with the pursuit of bigger, better and, above all, more. It would thus be a society with a higher level of contentment based not on a negative lowering of expectation, but on a positive withdrawal from the pursuit of unsustainable acquisition. With the growth of self-assurance it would also become a society of greater tolerance or even the celebration of difference, based on a shared understanding that autonomy and self-expression for oneself depend upon a reciprocal arrangement that recognises the individuality of others. And, as in all other societies that have produced a surplus within the historic constraints of their time, there would be a renewed interest in art, culture and spiritual values.

So, assuming that access to good housing, education, work, caring, physical and mental health and a decent environment were all in place (for there is a hierarchy here), we might begin to measure well-being in the following terms: contentment, control over one's own life, tolerance leading to celebration of difference, a deepening and widening of culture and a greater acknowledgement of temporality. These might sound like rarefied indicators, but it is important to have a clear idea of what we are seeking to achieve. Only then can we focus on how the imaginative and careful development of larger brownfield sites could contribute to our longer-term aspirations.

Drew Stevenson
University of East London, Dec 1999

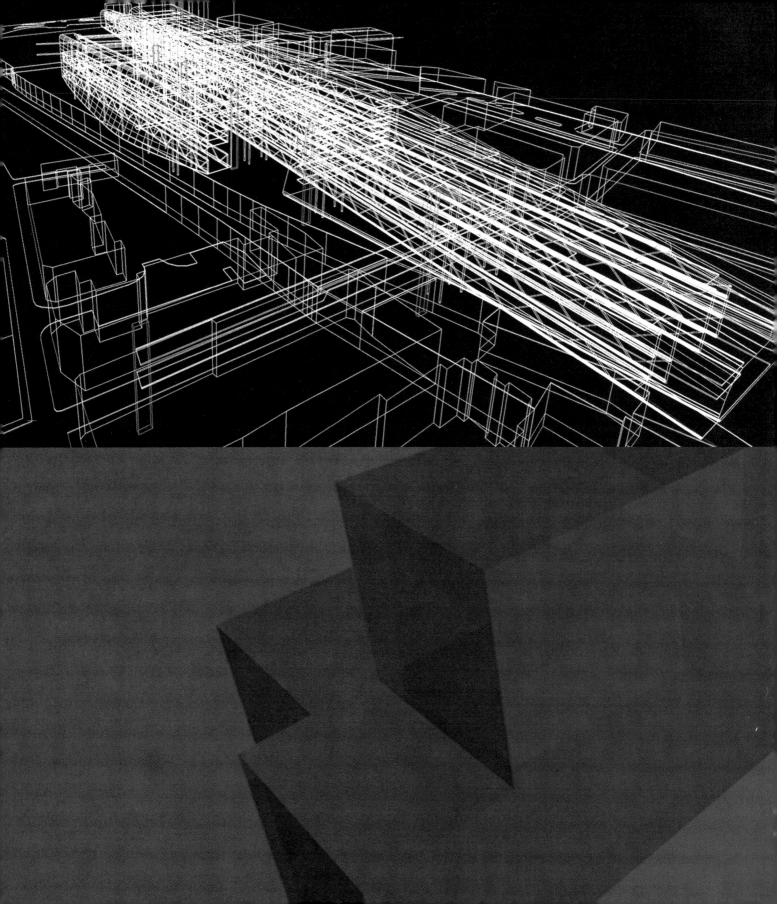

Brownfields, waste lands, the sites of obsolete infrastructures and forgotten industries are present in all large cities, and latent in their futures. These places are marked by inertia, and the longevity of their isolation can be extraordinary. In the case of Bishopsgate GoodsYard, the period of isolation is more than 30 years, despite its strategic location flanking the City of London. In other similar territories periods of isolation in excess of 50 years have been noted. This suggests a blind spot, a kind of unwillingness or inability to see such places that becomes gradually institutionalised until it becomes a collective response. Ways of living and working grow up around these places, encasing them so that it becomes difficult to perceive them at all. Exiled from the present and from the future, they are experienced only as exterior frames or borders to more vital urban spaces.

ALTERED PLACES

Michael Weinstock

Brownfields, waste lands, the sites of obsolete infrastructures and forgotten industries are present in all large cities, and latent in their futures. These places are marked by inertia, and the longevity of their isolation can be extraordinary. In the case of Bishopsgate GoodsYard, the period of isolation is more than 30 years, despite its strategic location flanking the City of London. In other similar territories periods of isolation in excess of 50 years have been noted. This suggests a blind spot, a kind of unwillingness or inability to see such places that becomes gradually institutionalised until it becomes a collective response. Ways of living and working grow up around these places, encasing them so that it becomes difficult to perceive them at all. Exiled from the present and from the future, they are experienced only as exterior frames or borders to more vital urban spaces.

ALTERED PLACES

Michael Weinstock

ALTERED PLACES

This perceptual dislocation is compounded by the problems of scale and of labyrinthine patterns of ownership. Many brownfields are of such a size that the assimilation of the site back into the city as a singular and integrated project has been impossible. What happens instead is the slow accumulation of smaller, linked projects on the periphery of the brownfield. These smaller projects and their associated residential groups are perceived as autonomous, and so undergo independent cycles of decay and regeneration. Small scale interventions and renewals establish new and different connections. Orientations to public spaces and programmes are changed, shifted downscale so that they no longer focus on relations to a single large territory. This tends to strengthen the boundaries, making them more opaque, and accelerates the dislocation of the interior of the site from the city.

It is not merely as an expedient response to the increasing pressures on the market, ever hungry for land as that is, nor solely to relieve pressure on greenfields that makes the regeneration of brownfields so vital a task. The fascination that these places have for us is a measure of their availability for the contemporary imagination of the future city. They are part of the speculative engagement, both topographical and theoretical, with spaces in-between, and with boundary conditions. Simultaneously real and imaginary, these sites are part of the fabric of the material city and yet they offer a latent domain of ideas. It is their separateness that makes them available for imaginary futures, precisely because they are unattached to function. These are the places where new forms of architecture and urbanism can emerge, and this is what makes their regeneration central to the project of the future city.

This does, however, present a dichotomy, as ideas about regeneration and the birth of the new architectures have had strikingly different trajectories. The social paternalism that dominated the discourses of architects and urbanists in the early part of this century was founded on egalitarian ambitions for the liberation of the poor and disadvantaged. New architectures were born from this drive, with new methods of building, and authorities expanded to administer and control vast building programmes. These municipal authorities built not only housing, but parks and schools, clinics and lidos, with the conviction that they were building not just neighbourhoods but a new society. Regeneration has quite a different set of associations, initially strongly located in the environmental discourses of recycling and sustainability. It is not a coincidence that now social responsibility has a wider, a global rather than local sense. The tension between these two sets of ideas and their separate associations is a crucial issue of urban renewal.

There are a limited number of suitable sites for regeneration, as strategies for reworking of toxic brownfields are difficult to initiate, and the assertion that such sites can be easily cleansed often arouses distrust. It is not just a matter of better marketing or superior geotechnics, for there is a barely repressed anxiety about carcinogenic dumps that pervades the consciousness of the city. Smaller sites are a problem too, more difficult to transform into urban developments, particularly for anything other than individual houses. Nor will there be much of a future supply of brownfields, as fewer sites are allowed to become derelict. Research shows that there are about 75 such sites in London at the moment.

Strategies for regeneration generally are easier to initiate when they involve the recycling of redundant buildings, as this adaptation is in itself an urban skill, and one that we are accustomed to. The better and more attractive buildings are already taken up by private initiatives, and in housing in particular this was soon followed by market trends. Such market driven initiatives are not incompatible with innovation, but their very success drives up their desirability, their imagability, and subsequently their price. The conversion of redundant warehouses into 'loft' spaces was once only for the artists and squatters, the marginal but vital elements of society. Today, occupation of such spaces is far more widespread. These spaces are becoming increasingly expensive, and are dominant in areas close to the financial City next to Bishopsgate. It is tempting to dismiss loft spaces as little more than a manifestation of the image of celebrity living that we see endlessly rehearsed in magazines and films, to an overly aesthetised version of an authentic industrial past. It is important to recognise that the inherent quality of the loft spaces is its openness and flexibility, and that this makes it capable of sustaining many different kinds of living and working.

Regeneration cannot begin with reproducing the spaces of the past. The structural changes to society brought about by the post-industrial dematerialisation of the economy are hardly completed, but their consequences are upon us. Social space was once strongly linked to the idea of the neighbourhood, the locality. The idea of what is 'local' is more difficult to define today. We are more mobile, our social and work relations spread over a larger area than in the past. There is, in consequence, an emergent sense of locality as something dispersed, a patchwork of people and places united not by proximity but by our ability to move between them by car, train bus or the tube. We join them up by our daily and weekend journeys, and it is these journeys that constitute the connections, the networks and flows that are essential for contemporary urban life. This kind of connection gives a quite different sense to 'locality' than the traditional neighbourhood of the historical city, in which 'local' is a bounded space, defined by proximity. Regeneration should begin with new connections, inflecting existing patterns of movement and making diverse connections to existing flows. Access comes first.

Demographic changes to society also require a rethinking of the kinds of domestic spaces that are built, and of how they are grouped into urban forms that are differentiated enough to become places. Much has been made of the estimated demand for a million homes in London and the

South East over the next two decades, but what is less frequently remarked is that 75% of these new homes are expected to be for single people. Fewer people marry young, more stay single and for longer, more divorce and all of us are longer living. Single homes will colonise large areas of the city, and this will change the sense of what can be the identity of a place. Places are where your parents lived, where you came from, where families lived. Places have an identity.

It is useful to look at this emerging context of urban solitude and individuation, and to reflect on identity. In fact, we are more accustomed to think of identity as a set of attributes of a person rather than of a place, as a relationship between individuals and their possessions. A large part of our sense of self is constructed out of the meaning that we attribute to the objects in our lives, the possessions that we have and those that we covet in order to construct our personas. Objects here include books, images and sounds, as literary and cultural sensibilities are part of our furniture of our lives. We can and do rework this self-definition, constructing new cultural identities for ourselves from time to time.

We are not bound by our familial inheritance in the same way that people were in previous times. Identity is not inherited, but constructed. This understanding can be extended to the reconfiguration of places and the invention of new ones. It implies that identity in a place is neither inherent nor permanent. It is something that the architect and urbanist must actively seek through the forms and materials of the buildings and spaces, and in their relations to the city as a whole.

To what extent the combination of imagination of the future architectures and the social and environmental agendas can be used to transform the obsolete railway yard into a place can be seen in the competition entries that focus on urban identity and spatiality. Bishopsgate Goods Yard has many of the features discussed above – it is large, difficult to perceive as a whole site except from above, and forms the northern boundary to the vitality of Brick Lane and Spitalfields. Built in the last century close to the

REGENERATION CANNOT BEGIN WITH

centre of the City of London, it is over a kilometre long, and its interior spaces have been abandoned since a catastrophic fire destroyed its upper floors in 1965. The massive vaults and exterior walls survived, although not entirely unscathed. It presents a closed form, its battered walls and dark barred openings enclose brick vaults. On its horizontal roof deck perch sheds, portacabins and construction huts, hunched like brooding gulls awaiting a storm. Rail lines and small road traffic routes pass through it in tunnels without offering perceptual or physical access to its interiors. It conforms to all the parameters of perceptual and functional dislocation that mark lost territories.

Thatchers' high tide of unfettered commercial development in the City has washed up against it, only to recede leaving it untouched. It exists within sight of the revitalised Liverpool Street Station, yet it remains unseen. The community of Spitalfields, the home of successive waves of immigrants (Huguenots, Jews and now Bengalis) pulses with dense and vital life on its southern edge, but turns its back on the "terrain vague" of the Bishopsgate Yard. The existing Brick Lane Sunday market occupies adjacent streets, tunnels, interior niches and some of the abandoned lots on the periphery. The territorial occupation of the market has expanded and contracted over the years, conforming to an opportunistic but somehow indeterminable logic. On certain summer days tourist groups are conducted around the sites where Jack the Ripper performed his surgeries, and yet the site remains separated from its own histories.

Place and space – what is the point in differentiating between these words? In a general sense we can say that "place" is a site of social experiences, of cultural and historical associations, and that we move from one place to another. Places have characteristics that are social and sometimes political, qualities that are somehow human. Space on the other hand is more abstract, a mathematical term for a kind of fluid ether that suffuses all places, and which all places contain. Place is a portion of something larger, of continuous and unending space. These are ancient distinctions and so it is a little strange in this new century

when both architects and urbanists legitimise their practices by claiming to be space makers.

The stronger the rights and privileges of the individual, the weaker collective identity becomes, destabilised and left without any recognisable cultural references. Space replaces place. The older forms of public places, the squares, parks and streets that we have inherited, were related to a certain pace of living, to social exchange and spoken language that was conducted by quite a different society to today. In newer urban spaces these relations cannot be achieved in the same way. The pace of life is different, determined more by mobility and need for connections and information than by local histories and events. Distance is collapsed, and the network of connections and movements loosens the bounds of places localised in time.

Many current urban design plans demonstrate a poverty of resource, and show a reluctance to acknowledge the qualitative failures of conventionalised processes for metropolitan scale urbanism. Proposals developed directly from historical models of public spaces, however much they are adapted to a new context, inevitably incorporate outmoded social practices and ways of using spaces. To treat history as a source book, as a colony to be plundered, is a procedure with a particular appeal for those who regret the passing of imperial cultures. The denial of historical models as an authority for a contemporary architecture means the rejection of the idea of archetype, and of the permanence of standard forms of housing and public spaces. To attempt to formulate a new urbanism and architecture on a formal or picturesque variant of the past is therefore self defeating, and carries with it the guarantee of the inappropriate and redundant. The inertia of the brownfields will not yield to pastiche but requires new instruments.

The existence of inherited urban spaces carries an implication of continuity and of a future existence – the continuing presence of the past posits the future. The past and the future are not implacably

REPRODUCING THE SPACES OF THE PAST

opposed. It is unproductive to imitate the past, and yet it is not necessary to eradicate it either, as there are already marked changes in the concepts and materiality of some new urban spaces. The materiality of the boundaries between interior and exterior space, between public and private territories, is no longer so relentlessly solid and opaque. The increasing transparency of such boundaries is accompanied by less rigid territorial demarcations. Spaces flow into one another, programmes are not so strictly confined within the building envelope, where connections and co-existence are enhanced.

There are new kinds of spaces that we use in a quite different way to those of the past, and they are often controlled by codes and tickets that give rights of passage and anonymity for limited units of time. These include the waiting rooms and transit zones of railway stations, transport interchange spaces, the spaces of engagements with computers, media and cash machines, hypermarkets and multiple retail spaces. They are described as spaces of transit, of assemblies of solitude and consumption where communication is by codes and images rather than conversation. It might seem that such spaces are anti-urban, in the sense that they deny all that we used to value in historical places. In consequence they have been relegated to peripheral locations, and have received little architectural or urban attention. However, the experience of these spaces is central to contemporary existence, and we are bound to integrate them into our designs for future places.

As these new spaces and programmes have displaced some older ones, it is logical to assume that future needs cannot be entirely projected from the present. There will have to be a dialogue between new places and their latent future – an inherent flexibility in the urban forms and systems that allows future changes. Diversity of uses and functions as well as adaptable spaces will help to avoid the potential isolation that is always the consequence of redundancy. This adds another requirement to a successful strategy, so that it must be unclosed and not wholly reducible to a rigid set of prescribed forms and spaces. It should take as its direction

Bishopsgate Goods Yard lies west to east across the city, massive and lumpy, like the fossilised carcass of an ancient saurian, a bone yard of forgotten railway tracks and darkened arches, dust breeding silently in the darkened spaces of its deep interior. Its forgotten territories are too long matured, rotting under a dense accumulation of abandoned and unexcised histories.

the recognition of group as well as individual dynamics and the episodic, ephemeral nature of metropolitan experiences.

The erosion of skilled manual work permanently linked to an area, a localised industry such as the printers of Clerkenwell, or the furniture makers of Shoreditch and Hoxton, has further loosened the connection of the identity of place with work programmes. Areas become more economically homogenous, they become identifiable by property types and prices rather than by trade or industry. Work is no longer solely determined by what is available locally, and there is a shift to less stable patterns of employment. This volatility is accompanied by social polarisation, that in turn leads to increasing spatial and territorial separations that is the antithesis of urbanity.

The role of mayor was crucial in the regeneration of Barcelona and of Bilbao, not only in encouraging and directing the political willpower, but also in the commitment to innovation and quality in new architecture and urban spaces. An important instrument in the regeneration of New York, and also of Barcelona, was the construction of a several kinds of public spaces and linked pedestrian networks independent of the road systems. Invested with excellent design and materials, these new paths and spaces thread through the city, linking parks and plazas, external squares and interior spaces by cutting through buildings and blocks. London needs to adopt such an enlightened strategy for its public spaces, and the role of Mayor of London will be as crucial here as it has been in other cities. English parks as they are now, are large set pieces inherited from the best periods of municipal provision, and unfortunately fallen on lean times. Many of them are dangerous and derelict, suffering from years of under investment and neglect. Once in disrepair, they become further vandalised and the process of degeneration accelerates. Where do children play games, where are the places of informal outdoor games and the ice rinks, where are the places for events and activities other than the tourist gaze which seems to be the sole remaining function of the larger central parks? English parks are becoming isolated, cut off by heavy vehicular traffic, and are losing their social and spatial connections to the city. Reconfiguration is as important as renewal for the parks, from their present isolated condition into a linked series of spaces, a connective tissue that can provide for extensive flows and offer social spaces. This is an essential city-wide strategy that should accompany the regeneration of individual brownfields.

The new Mayor of London will also have another critical role, that of reviewing the planning system, and could bring a new urgency to its viscous processes. The lethargy of Planning Authorities and their procedures has helped to produce the broadening gap between the number of future homes needed and the number actually being built. The re-engagement of local authorities in this important issue can begin with a commitment to densification, to a programme to build a million new homes in London on the 70 brownfield sites that have been identified as having the potential for high density redevelopment. The revitalisation of areas of the capital city will achieve more socially and environmentally than the building of ten smaller, less dense cities spread over the South East of London. High density is preferable to low density, as larger numbers of potential users sustain transport connections and parks, schools and shops. It is important to recognise their mutual interdependence.

The traditional institutions of government are caught in a fundamental contradiction. No matter that governments wish to project community values, they are not able provide the means to construct them. What remains of the welfare state is under external and internal stress. From outside, the Government budgets are influenced by and integrated with global financial markets. From inside, political changes have all but eliminated the role of the traditional municipal authority in favour of a more managerial role. The result is a crisis for municipal authorities. The less the nation state provides for its citizens, the more pressing the need to construct alternative means for the future grows. The new partnerships of public and private initiatives erode the old certainties and egalitarian ambitions of the traditional municipal institutions. They lose their legitimacy and along with that they lose their identity. A residue of regulations is all that is left.

PLACES HAVE AN IDENTITY

Municipal authorities built much more than housing. Council housing was once an arena of investment for ideas about society, and to build social housing was an affirmation of modernity. Municipal authorities were then characterised by a paternalistic attitude of social provision, and the different social structure then required municipal expansion. Now the descendants of these municipal authorities are driven much more by political and managerial agendas that demand contraction rather than expansion. Economic restrictions of authorities demand the reduction of inherited debt. So much of existing Council housing is old, and ageing properties tend to deteriorate rapidly when maintenance budgets are insufficient. Coupled with years of under investment in the past, low and ever decreasing income from rents just cannot meet maintenance costs and expensive debt servicing.

As social housing was originally built for communities, tenancies were offered for life and were passed down to sons and daughters. But since 1980, under the "right to buy" policy approximately 2 million homes transferred from social ownership of Municipal Authorities to private ownership. 3 million council houses remain, but this is not a static situation, and it is not hard to imagine that in the future there will be no Council housing. Isolated and segregated council estates are increasingly stigmatised, and to be known to have an address in one of them is to become one of the marginalised people of society. Homes on these estates are hard to let, unpopular and there are no waiting lists. Urban migration increases density in more vibrant areas, but leaves the segregated 'sink' estates with unwanted homes, as there is no one eager to occupy them. Blighted by social exclusion and depleted by urban migration, an ageing population is left behind, and as they in their turn die, so too will their estates. Now the extended period of contraction often means demolition, because there is nothing to do except to start again with new concepts, new developments.

Transfer of ownership to Housing Associations has been preferable and generally more socially useful than Thatcher's "right to buy", which, albeit modified, is a continuing policy of the current government. Housing Associations are more likely to have an agenda of social cohesion, as ownership is collective, not fractured into separate individuals who have little incentive to work together. They are private but non-profit making and can raise money to build. Housing Associations usually seek to develop a more complex social mix, and can find ways of making both private and co-operative ownership work together. This is just one of the new economic models at work now, based on different kinds of partnerships between public and private capital. Mutual and Co-operatives do already provide a part of the essential works of the city, such as health care and education, social housing and environmental services. These organisations are socially responsible and economically efficient, inherently socially inclusive. Partnerships are poised to play a bigger role in the 21st Century economy, and they are not bound to follow the rules of their predecessors, but free to develop a new approach. Their task is to provide the diverse and innovative spaces and places in which we will live.

Current ideas about community and social cohesion are often associated with mixed developments – private and social housing on the same estate, or in the same block. The idea of such mixed communities is not only the current Governments preferred policy but one of the unquestioned aims of contemporary urbanism. But it seems that new forms of architecture, and new urbanisms rarely live up to the rhetoric that has accompanied each new attempt. If we have rarely been successful in the past, what will the future bring?

Recent research from Demos shows that no matter how closely different people live to each other, they do not live as a community. Community is a concept strongly linked to locality, and as that has undergone a transformation, so too must the idea of community. Social cohesion is not produced by reconstructing the street and house patterns of the past, nor are the problems of social exclusion easily solved without resolving the potential conflicts and tensions between private and social dwellers.

continued p.78

Top of the Rock

ALSOP & STÖRMER

The visions we have of the future exist in order to allow ourselves to see a future. Very often these dreams, or visions, are driven by new technologies and practices. They result in an assumption that the past will be erased and replaced by a ìbrightî new beginning. The people who may reside in this vision maintain the same 'fears and hopes' they had in the past.

Life goes on.

This proposal leaves the existing fabric at lower levels and adds new layers of mixed functions above. The new additions act as a catalyst for the evolutionary regeneration of the existing fabric of the city. The spaces which exist below have a resonance which is impossible to recreate and whilst they have no specific function their presence is important. We see them evolving, in conjunction with the moonscape on top, as a place for cultural browsing, shopping, temporary events, short cuts, an umbrella etc.

The new 'rocks' hovering over the city are extreme in form. This is a deliberate act to make a clear distinction between old and new as well as to avoid the usual urban designer's vocabulary of **street, square and axis.**

The mixed use proposal is open to all as well as being open to the discovery of new uses. It is exciting, sustainable, friendly, challenging and beautiful.

It offers a model for remodelling and intensifying the use of the city.

I believe in the future
I'll live in my car
With my radio tuned to
A voice from a distant star
Some dogs howl at the dawn
And lightning brushes the
edge of a thunder storm
I live with these
hopes and fears

© Paul Simon

Alsop & Störmer
Will Alsop
Mike Booth
Tim Thornton
Charles Calvert
Frederico Grazzini

ARTHUR COLLIN ARCHITECT

Left. Model from north side

Below. Underneath the timber towers
social and commercial activities flourish
and fill the open spaces inside and around
the viaduct with life.

City lives

A vision for Bishopsgate goodsyard
prepared by Arthur Collin architect with Büro Happold

This proposal aims to engender a
greater sense of responsibility for
public space and create a more
sophisticated hierarchy of enclosure
from public to private.

Ambiguous public space is reduced
significantly so that what remains
makes a positive contribution to
urban life. All public spaces are
multi-purpose and any excess
circulation space has been removed.

The site combines a low-rise and a
high-rise typology – courtyard
housing and apartment towers.

The existing brick viaduct is mostly
retained, the arches below
containing public and commercial
activities. Pedestrian routes extend
Brick Lane market into the site. A
new urban square is created to the
north, opening the north facade of
the viaduct to the public.

A new double-level plinth is
constructed above the existing
viaduct, and its entire roof is
planted. The plinth incorporates
courtyard housing, public and
commercial activities.

A public square is formed on the
south side of each of the 5
apartment towers, providing open
green space at both ground and
plinth levels.

No car parking is provided, though a
car pool rents out electric vehicles.
All dwellings are reached from
ground level via the tower cores,
public squares and through a
number of 'mews' – small linear
openings cut through the viaduct.

The main building material used is
timber. Dwellings are all constructed
from standardised prefabricated pre-
fitted modules.

29

Rural and urban lifestyles are connected in a mutually beneficial partnership. The urban development is linked with a 'Rural Twin' in East Anglia, with which it will co-operate to provide work and commercial opportunities. A rail head connection handles deliveries of bio-fuel and food for a bi-weekly farmer's market. Waste products are removed by rail to the 'Rural Twin' for reprocessing and recycling.

The project includes a wide range of housing tenures, which are completely mixed. Live/work units incorporate 'front rooms' exposed to the street and separate from the rest of the dwelling.

Arthur Collin Architect
Arthur Collin, Paul Barnes, Jens Hoffmann, Francis Noon, Duncan Michel, Filip Visnjic, Cuong Trans-Viet, Steve Crosher, Matthew Smith, Buro Happold, Doug King

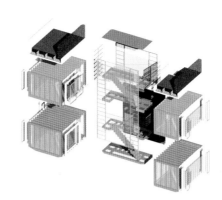

Towers are orientated in a north south direction in order to gain the best climatic values and prevent overlooking into the courtyards.

Left. Live work units are access through a mews.

TOWERS

URBAN AGRICULTURAL STRIPS

PRIVATE COURTYARDS

The central street is a social and commercial centre of the viaduct, providing a setting for the Brick lane market, giving access to open squares where people gather.

The courtyard house provides a flexible and luminous environment, giving the residents the possibility for outdoor activities ike eating and playing in the courtyard and sunbathing and planting on the roof garden.

Double height living rooms with sliding glass fronts gives the tower units a sunny internal spaces. Most flats have an incredible view over the city.

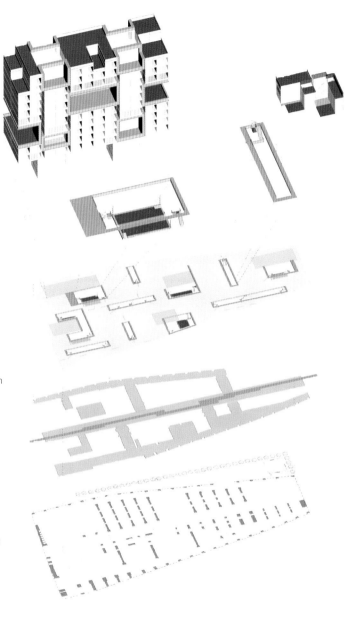

PUBLIC
COURTYARDS

PLINTH

PEDESTRIAN
NETWORK

CAR POOL

ENERGY

CONSTRUCTION

31

Skylab
Synthetic built environments for future living

B CONSULTANTS LTD

The aim of the scheme is to create a nexus across site boundaries, reflecting the diversity of the surroundings in a mixed development. In addition, the character in the architecture and geography of the Goodsyard has been integrated into the response.

There are eight main groups of buildings, plus some fringe refurbishment and new build. A range of densities and heights provide a total density of 500 people per hectare. All buildings have secure lobbies with community facilities. The buildings are designed for low energy use and provide gardens for the residents at multiple levels with an innovative environmental buffer zone.

Apartments
The majority of the buildings face south and use solar control devices such as external shades on windows. Sky gardens are located every two storeys and are shared by two or four apartments. Faced with translucent low-E polymer facades, these gardens uniquely allow many dwellings to receive sunlight from 160°. A spine corridor runs every two storeys on the north side of the buildings; this acts as a thermal buffer zone. The north facade is constructed from recycled broken bricks from the demolished railway arches, mixed with concrete.

Vehicles
A looped pool has 250 liquid propane gas vehicles for residentsí use. This reduces the number of cars required by 50%.

Biomass
An area of the old railway arches is kept to house a biomass system providing combined heat and power for residents and disposes of much of the site's rubbish.

Links
Pedestrian bridges and parks cross the railway cutting creating a street-level linkage to the south of the site. The new retail boulevard runs from Brick Lane beside the railway. Live-work units are added.

Parks
Public parks are located at ground level to the north of the site. Landscaping above the arches, about 5 metres above ground level, creates semi-public parks. These parks are closed at dusk to all but residents.

B Consultants
Tom Barker
Jamie Norden
Rupert Willard
Graham Jennings
Robert Webb
Matthew Innes

Apartment
Typology 'A'
Luxury duplex apartments
Floor area: 108m2
Well facilitated accommodation, with a low density of apartments, spectacular views and elevated gardens.

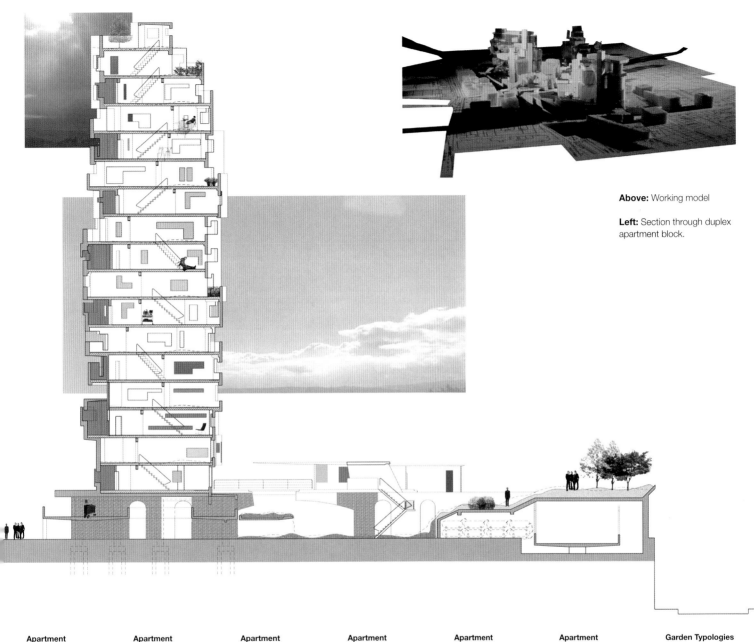

Above: Working model

Left: Section through duplex apartment block.

Apartment Typology 'B'
Single storey apartments
Floor area: 48m2
Medium density, low rise, single storey apartments.

Apartment Typology 'C'
Single storey flats
Floor area: 44m2
Medium - high density one bedroom flats.

Apartment Typology 'D'
Duplex family apartments 1
Floor area: 100m2
Medium density family orientated apartments.

Apartment Typology 'E'
Duplex family apartments 2
Floor area: 75m2
High density family orientated apartments.

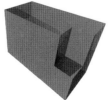

Apartment Typology 'F'
Single storey shared apartments
Floor area: 75m2
High density shared apartments suitable for students/ young professionals.

Apartment Typology 'G'
Duplex shared apartments
Floor area: 65m2
High density shared apartments suitable for students/ young professionals.

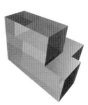

Garden Typologies
Green spaces throughout the buildings
Floor area: 48m2
Garden spaces dissolve the mass of the buildings

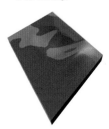

Living in the city

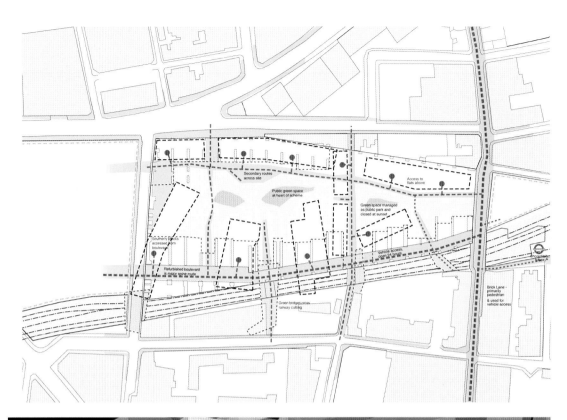

Diagrammatical master plan

Study of unit density

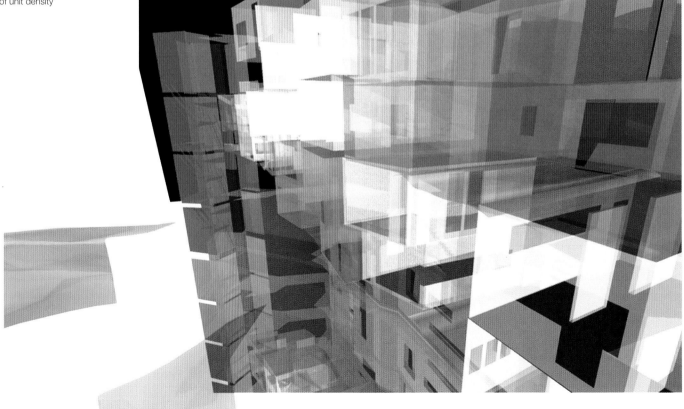

Diagrammatical long section

Luxury duplex apartment

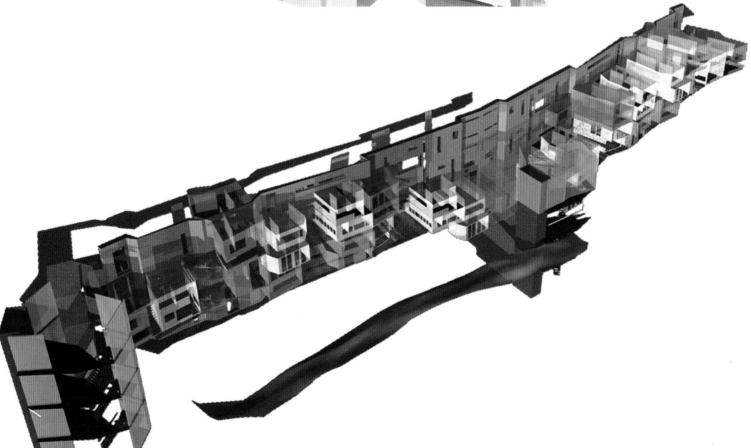

In the Living City

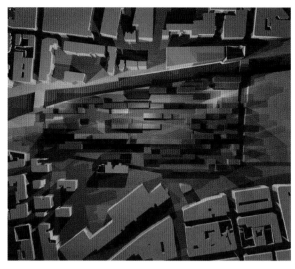

BRYANT PRIEST NEWMAN

The city must keep pace with changing lifestyles. This response acknowledges the microchip as the catalyst for change and applies it as the physical framework for the organic masterplan.

As with the organisation of a circuit board, common elements are here distributed across the site and linked by a series of linear routes and open spaces. Uses are meshed together both horizontally and vertically in bands which slide past, over and under each other. Usage and typology are adapted within the framework in a fluid transformation over time to establish a high density urban grain.

Parking at grade frees the deck level for pedestrians, producing intimate streets and spaces more appropriate to the scale of the houses and shops which they serve. Reducing street width also increases density which helps populate the external spaces and make them more vital places to be in. We want to rediscover the street of the past which served as a meeting place for neighbours and a place for children to play where a strong sense of community is engendered and crime against people and property is minimised.

The housing must be flexible to allow for demographic change. Movable screens are employed to borrow from gardens and terraces to increase internal space when necessary. Houses at ground level have rear gardens while the upper units use flat roofs/decks as gardens to maximise the available surface area.

This flexibility underlies the scheme from the macro to the micro and will help engender the urban renaissance which we both need and deserve.

Bryant Priest Newman
Mark Bryant
Larry Priest
Richard Newman
Dean Shaw

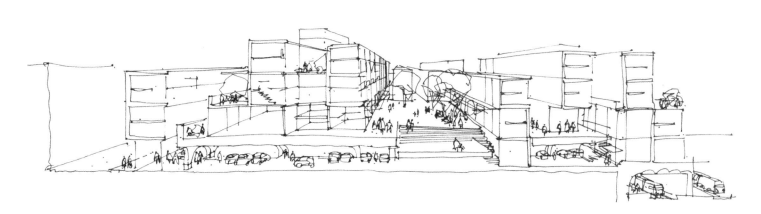

CARTWRIGHT PICKARD

The design proposals include:-

Street Level:
• Within the railway viaduct arches carparking for dedicated use by residents and retail servicing is provided.
• Live work units and light industrial workshops are situated adjacent to the railway boundary, also within the existing arches.
• Commercial office space is provided in a new building facing Brick Lane.
• A central area of viaduct arches are demolished to create a public park.

Park Promenade Level
• Retail and leisure uses are accommodated within the retailed viaduct structure which might include.
• Tesco Metro, Health club and gym, internet sales and archive storage units.

First Floor/Top of Existing Viaduct Structure
• Family residential dwellings with private gardens and semi-private communal gardens for apartment blocks.

Second to Sixth Levels
• One, two and three bed flats with balconies and/or roof top gardens for family units.

Tower
• Public space at ground level connecting to a cinema complex, restaurants, offices and ten floors of residential apartments with sky-deck winter gardens with south facing orientation.

Cartwright Pickard
James Pickard
Christopher McCarthy,
Battle McCarthy Engineers
Keith Blansuard, Yorkon Ltd

Bishopsgate Village
an Urban Lifestyle Vision

Our principal objective is to create a successful vibrant community with a distinctive sense of place and identity that will encourage a lasting sense of civic pride for inhabitants. The hierarchy of public, private and semi-private spaces is carefully integrated by circulation and movement patterns across the site. Clusters of dwellings unified by fully glazed atria, wintergardens, secure communal gardens and the careful use of materials, will form a recognisable neighbourhood.

Mixed Use Development
A sustainable living community relies on local economic activity and requires provision for living, work and trade. Robust and flexible buildings that incorporate the needs of this community are required. Affordable housing is not segregated but carefully integrated with privately owned and privately rented housing.

Access/Transportation Issues
Greater use of public transport is encouraged and a green park links Brick Lane to the City.

Shoreditch underground station is repositioned directly under the tower.

Electrically powered Smart Cars are provided for each apartment in the tower.

The Smart Car lift also serves the underground platform level allowing newly adapted underground trains to take Smart Cars to the perimeter of the city.

Cycle paths are provided through the park whilst cars are generally kept off the site.

Orientation and Solar Analysis
The triangular form and height of the tower minimises overshadowing, ensuring maximum solar gain to winter and other gardens.

All landscaping is south facing which promotes bright sunny internal spaces.

A darrieus wind turbine at the top of the tower generates electricity to re-charge the electrical cars.

Construction
The buildings should be built using materials chosen to have least environmental impact and maintenance requirements.

Pre-assembly of building units such as floors, walls and roof panels will allow comfortable, safe factory conditions to prevail for the most important construction steps. It will also reduce time spent on site and hence disruption.

Circulation, Access and Transportation Issues

Encouraging the greater use of public transport and establishing a green park link from Brick Lane to the city via Broadgate and Liverpool Street are key considerations of the scheme.

• Pedestrian and cycle routes across the site create higher visibility of Shoreditch station, reconnecting the natural migration of residents towards nodes of public transport. It is proposed that Brick Lane at the end of the site be pedestrianised to aid crossing the site boundaries to Shoreditch.

• A new bus stop is proposed for Wheler Street at the end of the pedestrian route through the park.

• It is possible that the site may be extended towards the city (Commercial Road and Shoreditch High Street) further reinforcing the connections to the urban centre and enhancing the green parked spaces of the East End.

• Secure access to all dwellings is offered via communal entrances directly from Sclater Street and through the secure atriums of each residential block within the Park.

• Deck access balconies within the atriums/winter gardens allow informal chance meetings and increase the sense of neighbourliness and protection.

• Retail servicing access is achieved from Sclater Street remote from residential entrances.

• All car parking is concealed within the viaduct arches, thus minimising the impact of traffic on the site.

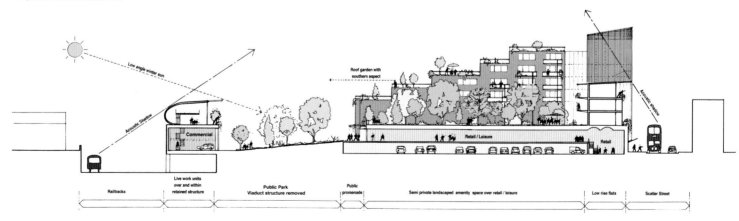

Orientation, Views and Environmental Issues

Solar Analysis

Fundamental to the site layout has been solar analysis which demonstrates:

• The new buildings have little shadowing effect on the surrounding site even when the sun is at low angle in winter.

• Tower is situated at the eastern point of the site creating little overshadowing to low rise residential blocks throughout the day.

• The triangular form of the tower also minimises the amount overshadowing towards the north.

• The height of the tower ensures maximum solar gain to winter gardens throughout the day.

• Most residences are south facing – utilising solar gain and reducing heating costs.

• The width between the courtyards ensures no overshadowing to adjacent residences.

• The terraces and stepped apartments allow morning and afternoon sun to enter blocks on an east west axis across the site.

• All landscaping is south facing which promotes bright sunny internal spaces.

Acoustic Buffers

• Live work, light industrial and commercial units on the southern edge of the site provide an acoustic buffer to the railway tracks.

• The raising of the apartment blocks on the northern edge provide an equal buffer against the traffic generation of the city to east routes.

Ventilation

• The residential block tiers and atriums promote cross ventilation and natural stack effect, drawing fresh, cool air across the flats and to the stair towers where warm air rises and is discharged via ventilation cowls at the stair tower roof level.

• The tower has a double skin wall creating stack effect through the tower height and drawing cool air through

• Prevailing winds from the South west are exploited

• Low energy design solutions to be integrated in technical, functional and socially effective ways avoiding expensive devices and equipment requirements "Keep the systems simple to use and easy to live with".

Construction Technology and Process

One of the main guiding principals for the design of the buildings is that they should be built using materials chosen because they have the least environmental impact and maintenance requirements. Where possible materials will be from renewable or recycled sources and require the least energy input for manufacture, transport and subsequent fabrication.

Pre-assembly of building units such as floors, walls and roof panels will allow factory conditions to prevail for the most important construction steps. Working under comfortable and safe conditions the quality of workmanship will be much higher than is conventionally achieved on a building site and accidents will be less likely. It will also reduce the time spent on site and hence the disruption to the community during construction.

To make best use of valuable natural resources, building components should be re-usable where at all possible so that when a building reaches the end of its useful life it can be disassembled, re-fitted and then re-built on another site. This is a further attraction of the pre-assembly approach that encourages re-use of resources.

Steel provides a material with excellent strength to weight ratio and which is easily worked into useable building components. It can be recycled and this is already the source of around 50% of steel used today. By using it sparingly, where its properties are fully exploited and with a view to its ultimate re-use or re-cycling, it is an important material unsustainable building construction.

Careful integration of mechanical and electrical services will allow for the replacement of services and plant that may reach obsolescence before the fabric of the building.

Standardised components will be developed to provide a diverse and flexible kit of parts. Dimensional co-ordination will allow a wide variety of building forms and materials to be used economically within a structural framework. It will be possible to dismantle whole or parts of buildings, rather than carry out wasteful and dangerous.

On site in north London, the prefabricated and fitted-out modules are lifted into position directly from the lorry.

Velocity - a solar urban village

BILL DUNSTER ARCHITECTS

Sunny cold morning – woke up early enough to catch breakfast in the trackbar before work – got my gear on in the shelter of the conservatory before freewheeling down the hillside – amazing view over the city – watched the first training riders shoot down the hairpins – colourful shapes half glued, half sliding down the rubber track – for once no traffic on the cycle highway to Bishopsgate – why do solicitors always ride full suspension? – I can hardly wait to pick up my new recumbent from the vault works – I still envy Sue lying in bed – watching butterflies in the sunspace – breakfast on the roof garden and a stroll to the studio under the hill – the nursery is sunny and the children can play on the grass – perhaps we shouldn't worry so much – looking forward to the weekend – my team's reached the semi final of the Peabody cup – must book an Espace for Sunday's trip – car pool seems to work well – lift goes straight to the car vaults and the electric Smart Cars have free parking in Westminster – these things are totally silent, zero emissions – running off solar electricity – itís a crime to drive anything else – even the heating and electricity is run off chip fat collected locally – our fuel bills are so cheap, I think I can increase the mortgage – the vaults are starting to make Camden market look tired – the space seems affordable enough to encourage experimental goods – and the workspace under the hill is now occupied by anyone from city dealers to graphics studios – managed to book help looking after the kids tonight – visiting some friends in the skyflats – its exciting watching the wind turbines – its fun just going home – weary commuters chat on the bikelift - before freewheeling down the suspension bridge and back to No 56 Hill Place.

Right: Low energy affordable homes
Superinsulated two storey homes with prefabricated fully serviced crosswalls incorporating wind driven ventilation with heat recovery, thermally massive construction and integral glazed sunspaces reduce the energy load to a fraction of a typical London house.

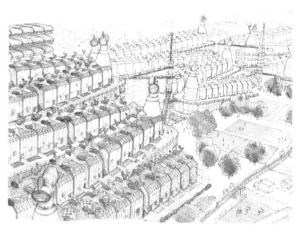

Live/work hillside
Hillside streets cycle to your front door on the fifth floor without pedalling uphill

Bike lifts raise both commuters and sports cyclists to the desired level giving them the potential energy to freewheel downhill to their house / workspace or use the racetrack.

Aerial view from south
The city block has become a small south facing hill town with its own communal facilities, cafes, nurseries, meeting places, workspace, sports facilities transplanted into the urban fabric of central London.

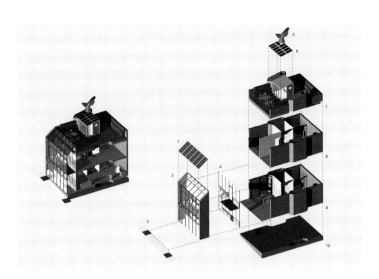

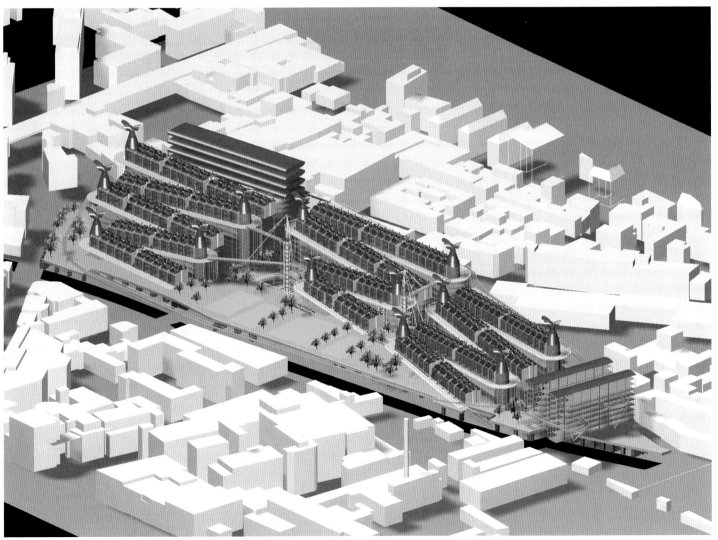

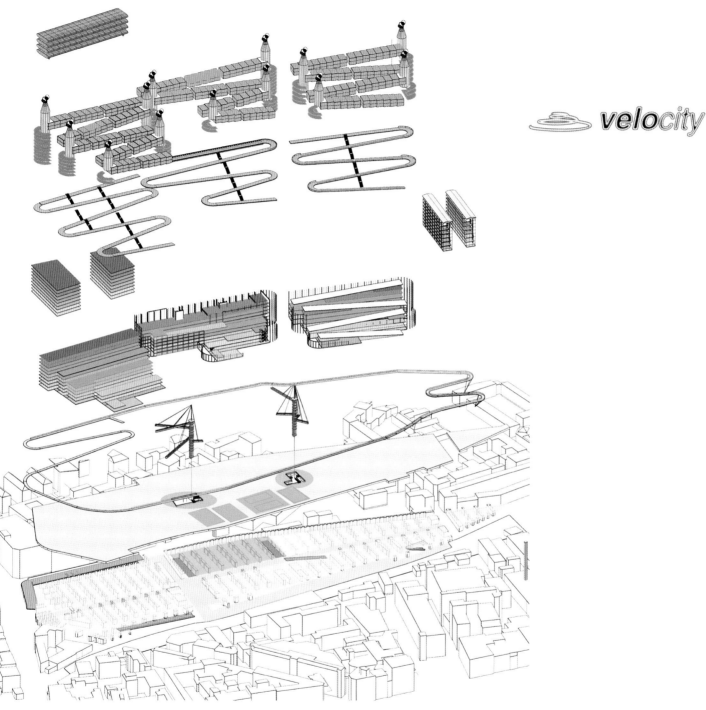

velocity

plateau level - site. Velocity uses whole area to create urban village

ramps up to all terraces for cycles and disabled

commercial levels with workspaces and atria

circulation malls at street level. using existing vault lines

electric car pool powered by PV cells on sunspace roofs

street level shops and trading spaces in the existing vaults

housing - premium end of terrace, 2 storey pre-fabicated maisonettes, and 2 person flats

meeting spaces around voids to vaults and towers to all levels - track bars

nursery / community spaces at ground level

playing fields - 5 a side football, basketball and tennis

rubber surfaced mountain bike track - from low level to high level

wind driven ventilation system / vertical circulation

Bill Dunster Architects
Bill Dunster
Leigh Bowen
Akira Yamanaka
Chris Twinn, Services Engineer
Jim McCarthy, Structural Engineer
Pooran Desai, Environmental Consultant

A working community

By placing workspace in the shade zones of the housing, whilst retaining reasonable daylight, live work is encouraged within the same development housed in multi purpose B1 workspace. Wind driven ventilation with passive heat recovery minimises fan use.

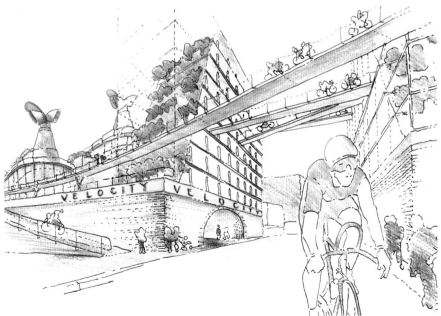

Brick Lane

Velocity entrance from Brick lane, with loft block and sports training track looping above road and grand arcade entrance to the vault markets.

Velocity has been designed to promote personal transportation in urban areas using bikes. Cycling is fuelled by carbon neutral biomass, improves the health of the rider and halves a typical households CO_2 emissions by avoiding car use. Velocity celebrates cycling culture The television rights on the annual Tour de Bishopgate have funded the entire PV installation for the car pool.

Living in the city

Multipli-city

Trends in society can only be directed by bringing clear visions into practice through strategic policies based on public support.

London needs projects considering new forms of urban lifestyles. This project integrates different lifestyles and social groups within one Superblock. The organisational form and architectural aesthetics create a typical new urban fragment offering new forms of use and new perspectives on social and economic sustainability and cohesion. Environmental sustainability will be reached by using innovative materials and installation technology.

City within the city

The site of 2.0 hectares will be occupied by one dense sculptural Superblock which offers a variety of housing typologies (62,000 m^2 living space for about 1,400 people) and additional urban programme. Its central interior area 'the city cave' and the landscape park next to it create a new 24 hour urban world.

Trends

The urban environment forms the battlefield for a new economy under construction and will change rapidly along with it.

Projects for urban development should anticipate these revolutionary changes in society. Challenged by the 'Zeitgeist', we should provide the conditions for new developments in contemporary lifestyles.

Research on urban population considers social groups by household types and financial income. More accurate categories would be diversification in lifestyles showing characteristics in social behaviour, demand for specific living space and urban programme, from household to lifestyle.

GROUP FOR ARCHITECTURE

+ WSA Consultants

A series of powerful trends can be traced that influence our way of living in the city. The urban environment forms the battlefield for this New Economy under construction and will change rapidly along with it.

Projects for urban development should anticipate these revolutionary changes in society. Our urban environment, challenged by the 'Zeitgeist', should offer alternatives by providing conditions for new developments in contemporary lifestyles. Relevant themes related to our profession should be defined.

Research on our urban population is principally based on a breakdown in social groups by household types and financial income. More accurate categories related to urban development would be diversification in lifestyles showing characteristics in social behaviour, demand for specific living space and urban programme.

From household to lifestyle

- Projected breakdown of households

- Calculation of households in m^2 on site

- Projected breakdown in lifestyles on site

24 hour lifecycle of the block

- Inhabitants

- Cave behaviour

- Synthesis: Multipli-city

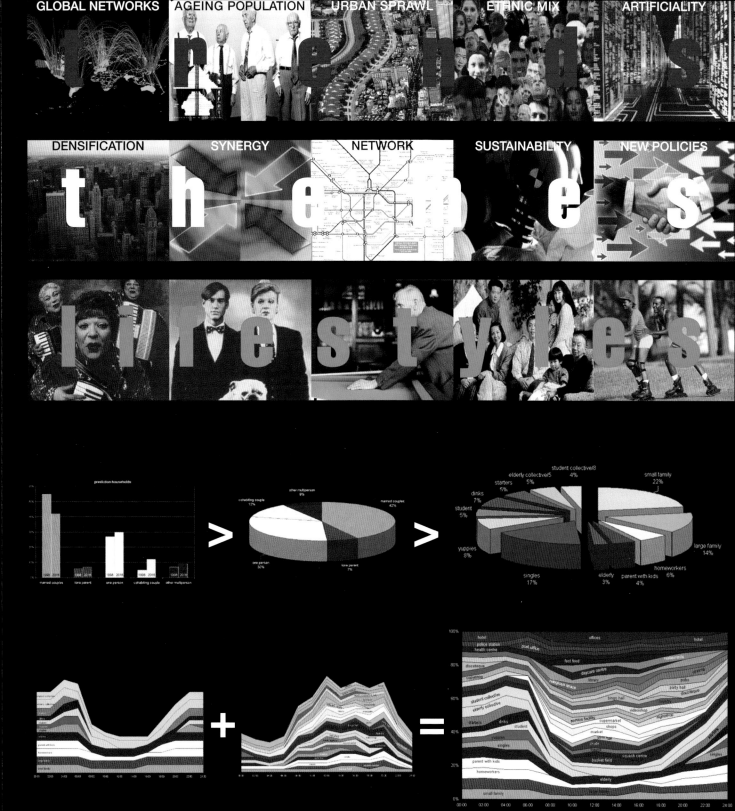

GLOBAL NETWORKS AGEING POPULATION URBAN SPRAWL ETHNIC MIX ARTIFICIALITY

trends

DENSIFICATION SYNERGY NETWORK SUSTAINABILITY NEW POLICIES

themes

lifestyles

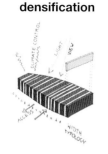

densification

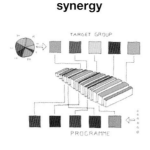

synergy

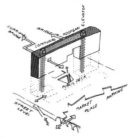

network

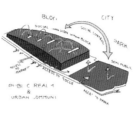

sustainability

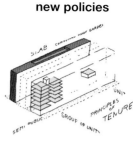

new policies

Design principles

Densification 'the layered city'
- the Superblock: a dense urban fragment
- 'stuffing' the city cave with 'dark' urban programme

Synergy   'the city as a melting pot'
- 'slicing & shaping' the block into of a series of slabs
- 'labelling' the slabs with lifestyles and typologies

Networking   'the networked city'
- internal/external infrastructure connected
- the urban programme in the block serving a greater urban area

Sustainability 'the eternal city'
- ensuring social sustainability within the block and the public realm
- 24 hour activities and economic sustainability of the Superblock

New Policies 'the managed urban development'
- new policies in public-private development/investment
- ownership per unit, per slab and tenure for the whole block

Group for Architecture
Maarten van Bremen, Folkert van Hagen, Jaap van Dijk, Tomaso Pini, Michiel Miedema, Will Sulsters, WSA Consultants

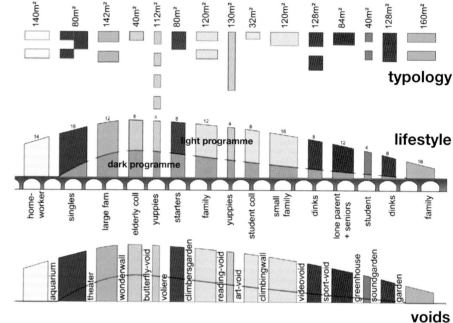

typology

lifestyle

light programme

dark programme

home-worker · singles · large fam · elderly coll · yuppies · starters · family · yuppies · student coll · small family · dinks · lone parent + seniors · student · dinks · family

voids

aquarium · theater · wonderwall · butterfly-void · voliere · climbersgarden · reading-void · art-void · climbingwall · videovoid · sport-void · greenhouse · soundgarden · garden

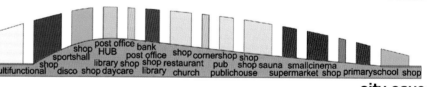

city cave

multifunctional · sportshall · shop · post office · HUB · bank · shop · cornershop · shop · disco · shop · daycare · library shop · post office · shop · restaurant · pub · shop · sauna · smallcinema · primaryschool · shop · library · church · publichouse · supermarket · shop

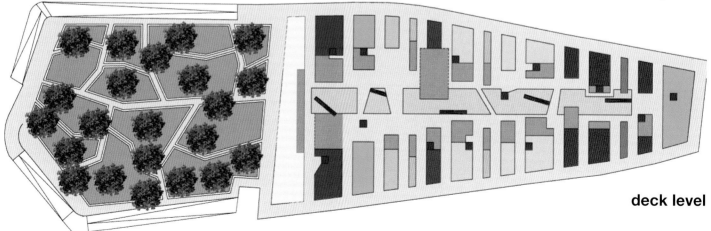

deck level

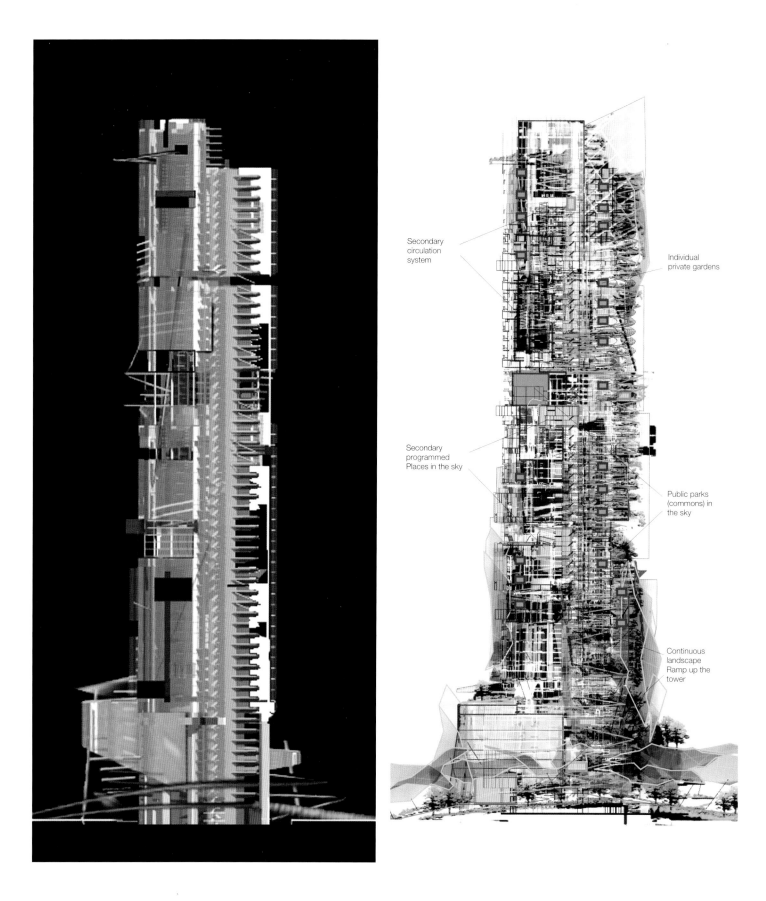

Secondary
circulation
system

Individual
private gardens

Secondary
programmed
Places in the sky

Public parks
(commons) in
the sky

Continuous
landscape
Ramp up the
tower

HAMZAH & YEANG

'Mixed-use, mixed-income, sustainable high density development...'

Primary Vertical Circulation

Tertiary Circulation Lift

Primary Circulation Ramp

Secondary Circulation Stairs

Primary Circulation Ramp & Landscape into building

Secondary Ramp Circulation

Social Sustainability

Our design concept can be described literally as the 'City-in-the-Sky'. The design takes a generic geographical model of the city with its inherent infrastructural systems, land zoning, physical environment and social systems and incorporate these it into the skyscraper building, to recreate the ground conditions in the sky to make high-rise housing humane, acceptable and superior.

Inherent in this concept are the following key design features of the tower:
• Continuous landscaping up the building
• Public parks in the sky
• Individual private gardens
• Secondary programs in the sky
• Secondary circulation system

Environmental Sustainability

Our approach to environmental sustainability is a holistic approach (i.e. it takes into account the entirety of the systems and functions of the ambient environment). The designed built system must minimise (and at the same time be responsive to) the negative impacts that it has on the earth's ecosystems and resources. The designed system can also contribute productively to the environment as well as restore and repair damaged ecosystems.

We contend that ecological design must consider the following aspects of a building:

• **External interdependencies** consisting of the designed system's relations to it's external environment and ecosystems.

• **Internal interdependencies** being the designed system's internal relations, activities and operations.

• **External-to-internal exchanges of energy and matter** being the designed system's inputs of energy and materials.

• **Internal-to-external exchanges of energy and matter** being the designed system's output of energy and materials.

Any design that does not take the above aspects into consideration is essentially not an ecological approach.

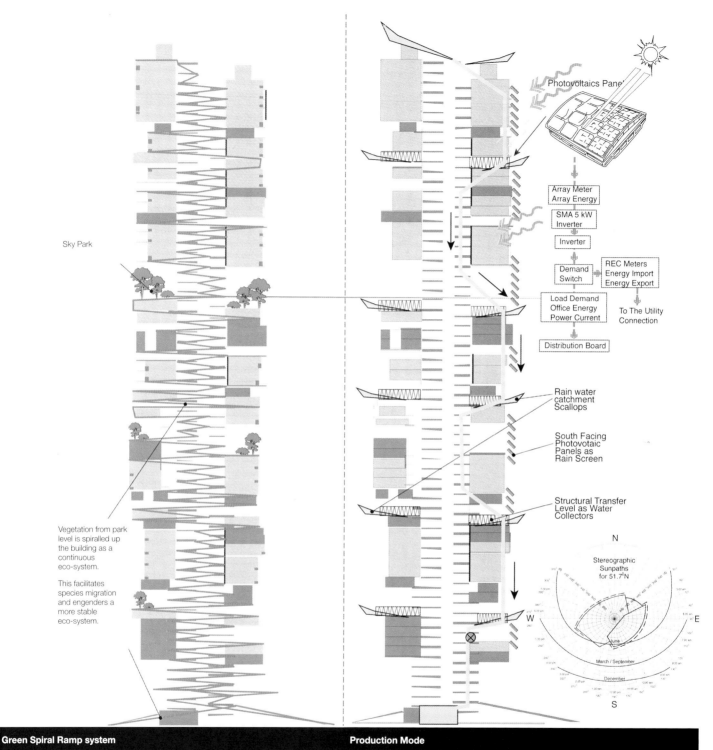

Sky Park

Vegetation from park level is spiralled up the building as a continuous eco-system.

This facilitates species migration and engenders a more stable eco-system.

Photovoltaics Panel

Array Meter
Array Energy

SMA 5 kW
Inverter

Inverter

Demand
Switch → REC Meters
Energy Import
Energy Export

Load Demand
Office Energy
Power Current

To The Utility
Connection

Distribution Board

Rain water
catchment
Scallops

South Facing
Photovotaic
Panels as
Rain Screen

Structural Transfer
Level as Water
Collectors

N

Stereographic
Sunpaths
for 51.7°N

W   E

S

Green Spiral Ramp system

Production Mode

External interdependencies

Considering that this site is a totally urbanized and "zero culture" site, the design strategy is to increase bio-diversity and organic mass by re-vegetating the site in order to rehabilitate the site's ecosystem. This is addressed by our provision of a park over the land and the adoption of a system of continuous planting up the towers (as "vertical landscaping")

Hamzah & Yeang

Ken Yeang, Andy Chong,
Chuck Yeoh, Ong Eng Huat,
Jason Yeang, Loh Hock Jin,
Gezin Andicen, Ool Tee Lee

Internal interdependencies

There are four levels of provisions for a building's internal environmental operational systems:

• Passive mode (i.e. low-energy design without the use of any electro-mechanical systems)

• Mixed mode (i.e. Partially electro-mechanically assisted systems that optimise other ambient energies of the locality)

• Full mode (i.e. Active systems, with low energy and low environmental impacts)

• Productive mode (i.e. Systems that generate on-site energy, e.g. Photovoltaic systems)

Our design strategy is to maximize the usage of passive-mode systems (because of its lowest level of energy consumption), with the remaining energy needs to be met by mixed-mode systems, then full-mode systems and productive mode systems (where affordable).

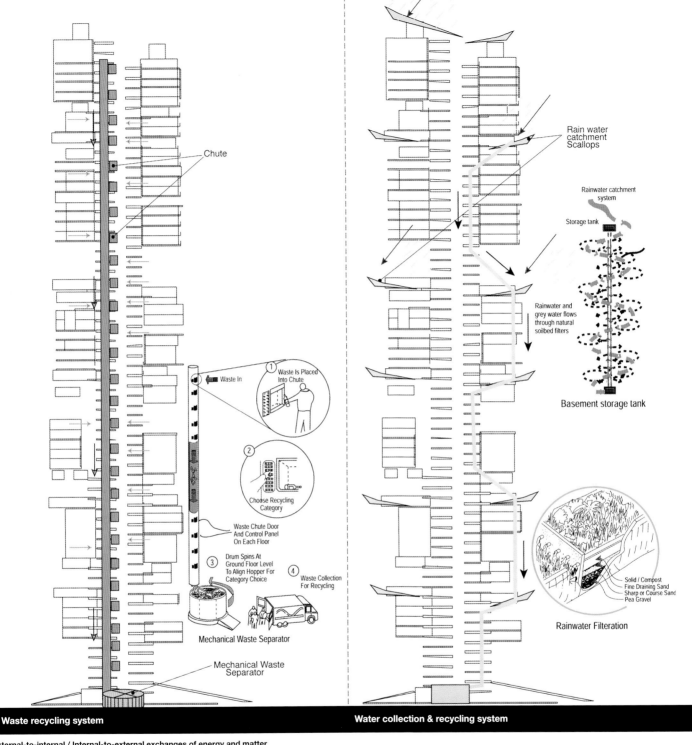

Chute

Waste In

① Waste Is Placed Into Chute

② Choose Recycling Category

Waste Chute Door And Control Panel On Each Floor

③ Drum Spins At Ground Floor Level To Align Hopper For Category Choice

④ Waste Collection For Recycling

Mechanical Waste Separator

Mechanical Waste Separator

Rain water catchment Scallops

Rainwater catchment system

Storage tank

Rainwater and grey water flows through natural soilbed filters

Basement storage tank

Solid / Compost
Fine Draining Sand
Sharp or Course Sand
Pea Gravel

Rainwater Filteration

Waste recycling system

Water collection & recycling system

External-to-internal / Internal-to-external exchanges of energy and matter

Our initial design strategy is to select materials based on their potential for reuse and recycling, in order to reduce the impact on the natural environment and to positively renew, restore and enhance the natural environment.

This includes the embodied energy and ecological impact of the use of energy and materials in the building which reflects the impact of production of the material or component (both globally and locally) at the source of manufacture, as well as the chain of activities leading up to its delivery to the construction site and it's eventual recycling (at the end of its useful life).

Our design strategy includes consideration of waste production and disposal in the life-cycle of the building. A central objective of our design method is to limit the quantity of materials and energy expelled by the building into the environment.

Other aspects considered are the re-use and recycling of building parts and building materials at the end of the building's useful life, and the management of consumer wastes during the use of the building (eg. through the use of a waste separator for waste recycling etc.)

City within a City

Cities are organisms, continuously in motion and hard to fit into a strict planning framework. Living in the city means more than just a collection of residential units. The situation of one-track single-use encourages social isolation, eliminates open communication, panders to spontaneous development of existential dread and egoism and thrust human relations and interactions into the background.

Living also stands for environment and the movabiltiy and is consequently tied to sustainability.

Living stands for structure, network and programme.

A maximum of supportable density, the opportunity for mixed-use and the partially integrated affordable housing at lower costs with constant quality standards also for the public open space.

To preserve the quality of life in spite of the increasing density has to be the central issue. Open public spaces become a substantial planning parameter.

Sustainable urban design

Seamless pedestrian network:

The architectural design exhibits a multi-faceted response to the requirements of sustainable urban design. Most significantly, pedestrian access has been given high priority. A seamless network of pedestrian paths allows the inhabitants to reach various locations on the site without undue interference from other modes of transport. This network also integrates articulated green spaces, gardens, overhead walkways and covered promenades. The pedestrian network is strategically interwoven with the grid and node system of public transportation.

Orientation, solar access:

The main orientation of the building complex is south-facing. The stepped massing of the two main wings of the design allows for maximum access to solar energy and daylight. The location of open spaces, children's play-areas, places of rest and physical activity is defined according to the cardinal points.

Mixed use:

The design programme includes residences, hotel, offices, and an integrated array of smaller and larger shops. To satisfy the programme requirements, a number of parking spaces are provided for temporary (commercial) and permanent (residential) use.

Hierarchy of urban spaces:

The differentiation and gradation of urban hierarchies are accomplished in the design not through artificial barriers and signs, but rather via the natural elements of massing, path layout, and vertical progression. While more public spaces such as shops and pedestrian paths are situated on the lower floors, more private spaces (e.g. residential units) are located primarily on the upper levels.

HELMUT RICHTER

Sustainable building design

The north-south orientation of the building volumes combined with a building volumes combined with a building depth of 10,00m -12,70m results in an optimum lightening condition. The loggias in the south side serve on one hand as climate control buffer zone (movable glass panels) on the other hand as a generous individual open space. An important issue is the cross-ventilation for all rooms. The access via arcades allows a reduction of elevators.The bridge connections which can be placed freely bring about a high level of flexibility. This access zone promotes communication.

An arrangement of organisation in private and semi-public spaces becomes possible.

Compactness, density:

The compactness, as expressed in terms of the "characteristic length" (i.e. the ratio of volume divided by building envelope) amounts to 4.2 [m] for the north wing and 3.4 [m] for the south wing. This translates into an appropriate level of compactness for both energy efficiency and potential for social interaction.

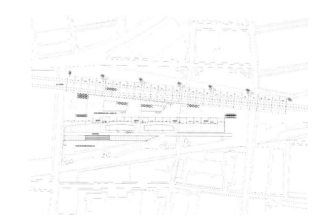

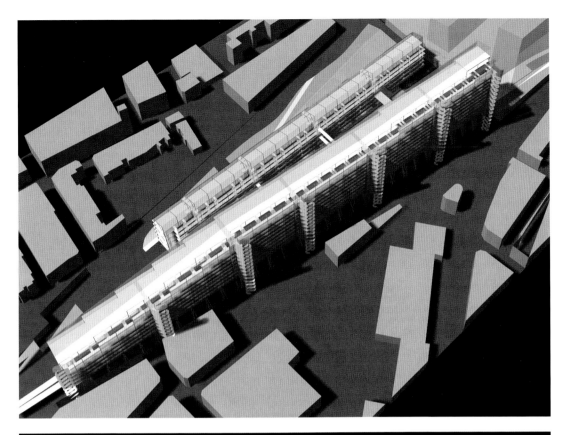

North view

South view

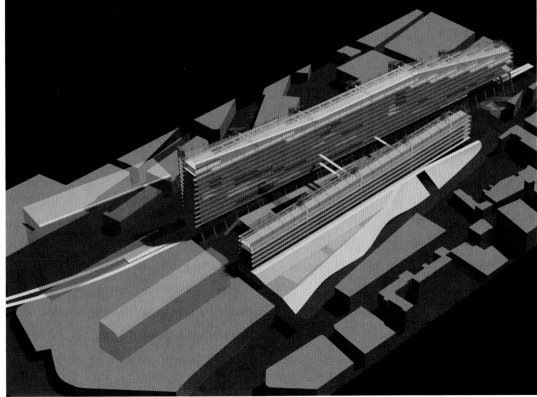

Energy conservation/generation:

The configuration of the building fabric combines a high level of thermal insulation with appropriate thermal mass. The U-value for the roofs and exposed floors is 0.15 W/m²K, for exterior walls 0.2 W/m²K, for the glazing 0.8 W/m²K, and for window and door frames 1.5 W/m²K. This combination of compact massing and the high thermal quality of the building envelope results in such a low level of heating demand that the building may be characterised as a 'passive building'. The heating demand can be expressed as the annual demand per unit heated area. The following diagram illustrates the demand for the project's two wings assuming both natural ventilation and controlled ventilation options. The year-round simulation for the building's thermal behaviour showed that no risk of over-heating in summer time exists. This is achieved in part due to the integrated solar control devices such as overhangs and movable blinds. Moreover, the design configuration allows for the integration of an array of south-facing thin-film photovoltaic panels. The location of these panels are shown in the design documentation.

Water collection/conservation:

The design incorporates a distributed system of water containers for the collection of rain water. The collected water will be used primarily for the irrigation of the green areas on the site and as water supply source for pools, fountains, and similar landscape features.

Material use/recycling:

The building construction materials are dominated by steel-concrete compounds, timber, and glass. It is anticipated that these materials will be specified in such a manner so as to include a large recycled portion. Moreover, the nature of the proposed construction facilitates the disassembly, separation, and reuse of the building elements/materials.

Space heating, warm water, lighting:

Based on the analysis of the available energy sources and use patterns, the design recommends a rather decenteralized mode of energy management. For example, residential

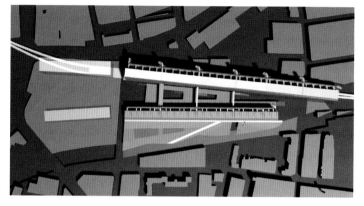

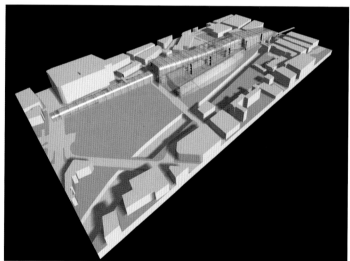

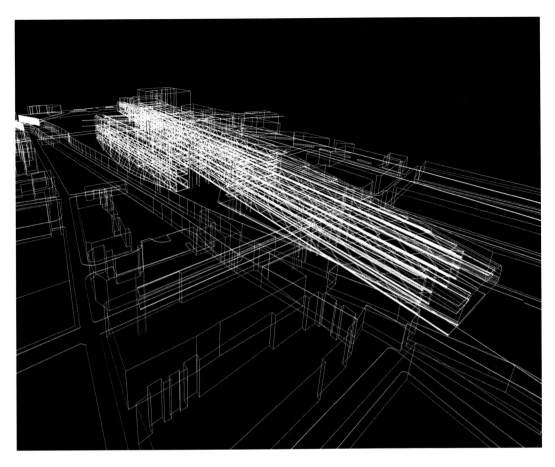

units can be served with highly efficient small heating systems that are responsive and user-friendly (e.g. controlled ventilation with heat recovery which covers the main fraction of the extremely small heating demand). It is very important to emphasise that this system allows for the user-based control (user override) as well as natural ventilation. The layout of the residential units allows for the use of cross-ventilation. The decentralized nature of the overall energy concept allows each individual residential unit to implement solar-thermal systems (integrated in the facade) for warm-water supply. Daylight is the dominant source for lighting of the spaces. The use of daylight is not only advantageous from the point of view of user well-being, but also represents the most efficient source of light from the energy standpoint. The glazed portion of the external walls amounts to 70% on the south side and 30% on the north side. The estimated average daylight factor in the south-oriented spaces in the residential units is 4%.

Sustainable construction:

Contemporary choice of construction materials for walls no longer consists only of bricks or concrete. These materials not only constitutes in flexible room enclosures and demonstrate unfavourable ecological balance. Steel and glass are easy to separate in the recycling process. Composite construction allows the structural dimensions to be minimised thus reducing costs and maximising usable space.

Materials/insulation:

Criteria used for the selection of the primary building materials and indoor finishes were significantly influenced by concerns pertaining to both environmental impact and human health. Such criteria required, among others, that materials do not contain toxic constituents and display no out gassing behaviour. Currently, alternative insulation systems (vacuum insulating elements) are being considered.

Ventilation:

The proposed controlled ventilation system is based on 100% fresh air intake. The efficiency of the heat recovery system is 80%. This is achieved in part by a sufficiently air-tight envelope. Furthermore, the operable windows allow the building to be run exclusively on natural ventilation if the users so wish.

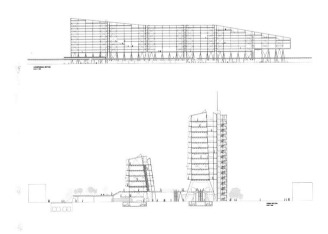

City Arcade – An Urban Living Prototype

HORDEN CHERRY LEE

Form and Scale

City Arcade derives its' form from European scale streets and arcades. These include The Albany, Royal Arcade, and typical smaller London Streets and mews. In this case City Arcade provides numerous north – south through routes interconnecting Spitalfields with Bethnal Green and Shoreditch.

Community and Privacy

City Arcade provides community and privacy from trains and busy city streets. They are orientated so all apartments catch the sun during some part of the day. Lifts, bridges and stairs animate the space connecting public circulation to generous private balconies which extend living and private space. Eucalyptus trees and balcony planting soften the Arcade and courts.

Eames

City Arcade's 'layered' elevations are informed by the playfulness of The Eames House, exploring a richness in the façade creating finely crafted layers and surfaces.

Integration

City Arcade is a fully integrated development, bringing into balance everything from living, work, leisure, retail, recycling energy concepts and hobbies with new concepts of mobility, entertainment; social mix, education and community facilities.

Mobility

City Arcade encourages environmentally sustainable mobility. Tube, bus and cycle routes have all been incorporated into the development. Ground level public space is maximised for the pedestrian. 'SMART' or Swiss Horlacher city electric cars are stacked vertically avoiding ground level or expensive basement parking occupying only 1.6% of the site area. (normal parking is 42% of site area) The 'SMART' car or alternative electric city car powered by solar cells enclosing the stacking system.

Prefabrication

City Arcade has been developed with the construction industry to achieve fully pre-fabricated residential units based on a module of 5m which is the typical width of London terraces. Modules can be delivered within 6 months to any European City from a central European factory.

'Lofts'

City Arcade creates 'loft' apartments which can be ordered, fully equipped or just as serviced spaces. Internal partitions and fittings are modular so each apartment can be laid out and constantly adapted to suit tenants' requirements.

Objectives

City Arcade is an affordable, sustainable, well designed space for living, working and leisure.

City Arcade Design Team:
Horden Cherry Lee Architects
– London (UK)
Stefano Angaroni, Stephen Cherry, Adrian
Fowler, David Franklin, Richard Horden,
Billie Lee, Peter Ludwig, Kwamina
Monney, Jurgan Schubert, Andreas
Vogler, Danielle Williams, Peter Zimmer
HL Technik – Munich (D)
Oscar Faber – London (UK)
OFFRA Generalbau Gmbh and Co
– Beverungen (D)
MCC smart Gmbh – Renningen (D)
Max Horlacher – Basel (CH)

1 The site is currently impenetrable from the surrounding area.

2 The proposed scheme is fully accessible from the adjacent street pattern.

3 The proposed plan stitches the site into its context

4 Completed units are assembled on site.

5 Highly glazed and flexible apartments with car stacking towers at each end.

6 Smart Car

7 Smart Car tower in Munich

8 Lobby level with multiple leisure uses for tenants.

9 Typical flexible apartment layout

10 Mixed uses at ground floor level accessed from public through routes and squares

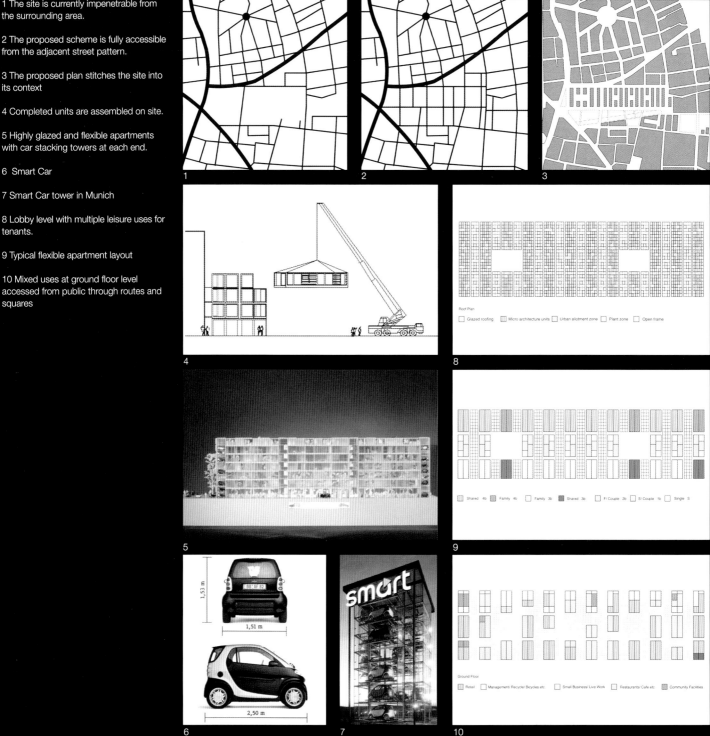

1

2

3

4

Roof Plan

☐ Glazed roofing ☐ Micro architecture units ☐ Urban allotment zone ☐ Plant zone ☐ Open frame

8

5

☐ Shared 4b ☐ Family 4b ☐ Family 3b ☐ Shared 3b ☐ F/ Couple 2b ☐ S/ Couple 1b ☐ Single S

9

6

1,53 m

BB · AF 92

1,51 m

2,50 m

7

Ground Floor

☐ Retail ☐ Management/ Recycler/ Bicycles etc ☐ Small Business/ Live Work ☐ Restaurants/ Cafe etc ☐ Community Facilities

10

Site Plan

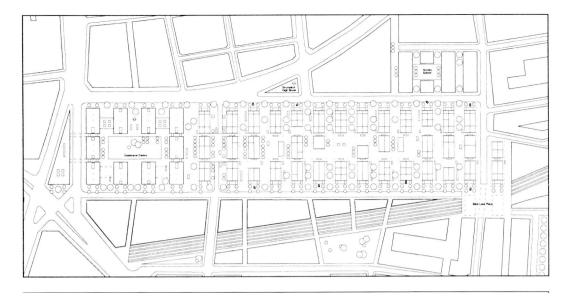

Typical apartment
Level one of arcade unit

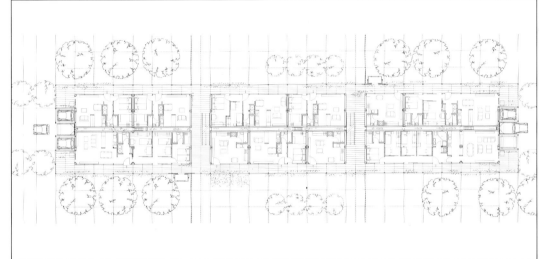

City Arcade elevation

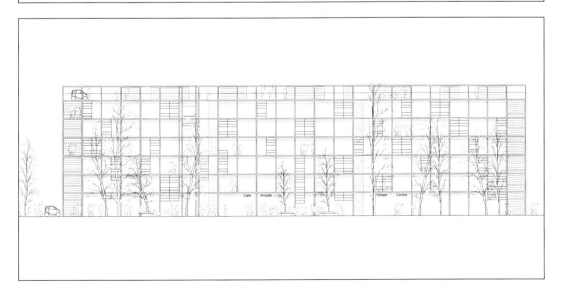

21st Century Party Walls
proposition and development strategy:

The immediate area is in a state of 'pressurised flux'. A rapid transformation of use and building typology is taking place close by. The City has bridged Liverpool Street and is encroaching into the Spitalfields area, displacing some of the newly 'activated' public spaces. The scale of the site and the 'undercurrents' of change that are taking place indicate that a highly deterministic approach would be inappropriate and likely to restrict or distort the opportunities for regeneration in the wider area by exclusiveness rather than inclusiveness.

This is reinforced by the wider implications of communication technology. Its effects on work life, home life and lifestyle are blurring the parameters used for designating spatial use. Hence it is becoming more difficult to conceive a 'total vision' of space which is fixed in time and place.

The essence of our proposal is the exploration of a strategy creating a variety of spatial uses that enrich the city as a place to live. At Bishopsgate, this is brought about by an analysis sensitive to the underlying characteristics of the site, its communities and location.

The proposal is 'street wise' in the sense that it recognises that a proportion of any development needs to be available for the most commercial of uses if it is to be accompanied by less commercial uses which generate diversity. Our strategy is presented as a 'tool box' for brownfield sites.

We have concluded that it is the issue of overlapping uses in both the contemporary-current sense (fixed/tangible e.g. housing commercial etc.) and the evolutionary/developmental sense (transient and experimental – markets, street festivals, short term uses – studios etc.) which are essential for creating a diverse city environment.

The strategy to achieve this is summarised in 4 diagrams. They describe the retention of the arches and improvements to the public permeability of the site (diagram 1). The creation of four distinct types of public space (diagram 2). The introduction of party walls as a mechanism for subdividing the site (diagram 3) and detailed development of the Slices defined by the party walls (diagram 4).

Ian Ritchie Architects
Ian Ritchie
Gordon Talbot

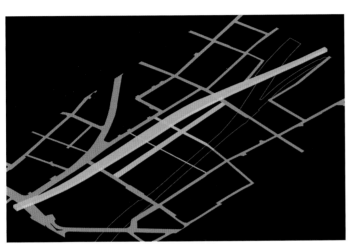

Diagram 1.
Retain arches and improve public access

By retaining the existing arches an immediate spatial resource is secured. This provides a continuity for the short term uses that have already been 'invested' in the site and have begun to 'activate' the undercroft.

The public permeability of the site at street level is improved by opening the north and south edges for public access, and introducing a public route between the arches. Two new north-south public routes are introduced across the site, one linking across the railway cutting.

Diagram 2.
Public space and landscape

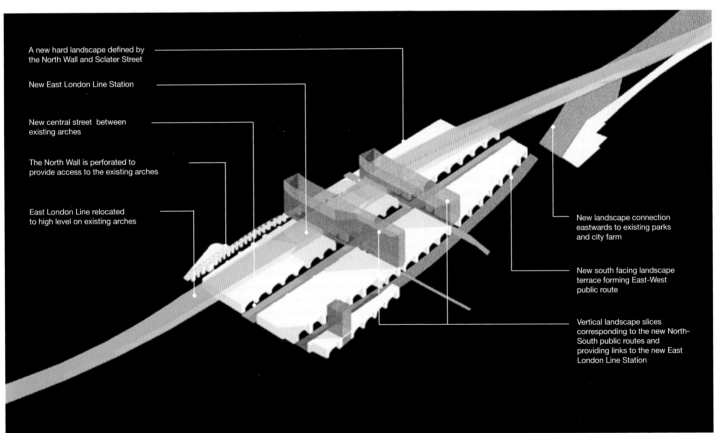

A new hard landscape defined by the North Wall and Sclater Street

New East London Line Station

New central street between existing arches

The North Wall is perforated to provide access to the existing arches

East London Line relocated to high level on existing arches

New landscape connection eastwards to existing parks and city farm

New south facing landscape terrace forming East-West public route

Vertical landscape slices corresponding to the new North-South public routes and providing links to the new East London Line Station

Diagram 3.
Party walls, Slices, diversity of use

The site is subdivided into 20 slices or 'burgage' plots. 4 orientated North-South and defined by the footprint of each individual arch. The slices are bounded by 'virtual' party walls which provide the vertical plot boundary and can be used as a mechanism to safeguard sunlight and daylight. The slices are 'served' by three defined zones: two located on the north and south perimeter of the arches, and the third located between the two arches. The defined service zones form part of the slice.

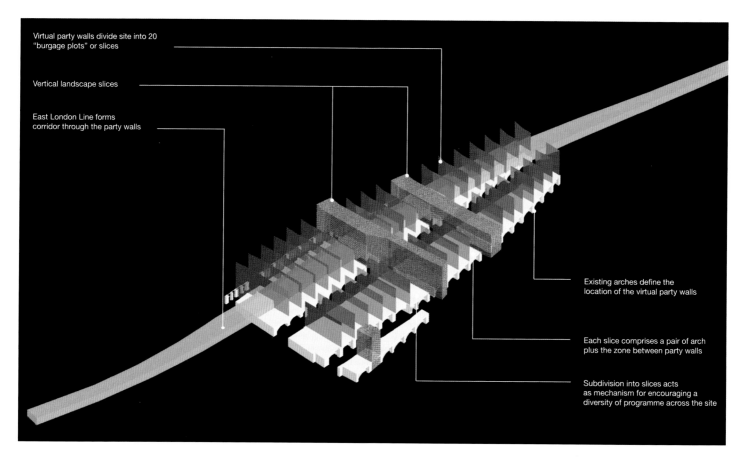

Virtual party walls divide site into 20 "burgage plots" or slices

Vertical landscape slices

East London Line forms corridor through the party walls

Existing arches define the location of the virtual party walls

Each slice comprises a pair of arch plus the zone between party walls

Subdivision into slices acts as mechanism for encouraging a diversity of programme across the site

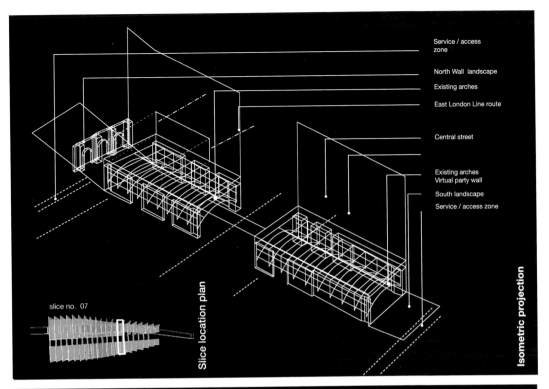

Service / access zone

North Wall landscape

Existing arches

East London Line route

Central street

Existing arches
Virtual party wall

South landscape

Service / access zone

slice no. 07

Slice location plan

Isometric projection

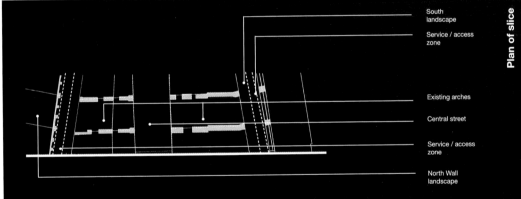

South landscape

Service / access zone

Existing arches

Central street

Service / access zone

North Wall landscape

Plan of slice

Diagram 4.
Detailed development of Slice

Slices

By subdividing the site into slices determined by the arches we provide a means of grading density across the site and providing the opportunity for a diverse range of uses to take up space with-in the site according to the time-scale of the development process and the self evident opportunities.

Virtual Party Wall

The slices are defined by virtual party walls. These are considered as an interfacing surface between slices. The party walls would follow "conventional" party wall principles. If developments are carried out simultaneously they could be shared (structurally). If the party walls are constructed on the boundary they would provide a right of support for the adjacent slice. Independent walls would be constructed off the boundary offering no right of support.

Slice Definition

Each "slice" is defined by:
> The arches below
> The north and south boundary
> The extended East London Line which passes through each slice at high level
> The public Landscape routes to the North and South edges of each slice
> The service corridors providing access to the "slices"

Each "slice" is provided with a suggested maximum plot ratio and residential density.

In order to develop each slice the following engineering principles should be considered if the development is to be supported on or through the existing arches:

A light weight development of up to 8 or 9 stories may be supported by the existing arches providing it only induces vertical forces, alternatively a separate support structure may be added by placing supports either through the crown or the buttresses of the existing arches providing that the new supports do not transmit any horizontal loads to the arches.

The width of the total site, which varies from 120m –55m this implies the following means of escape strategies:

stair on the north side of the site, one stair on the south side of the central street and one stair on the south side of the site, possibly a counter weighted stair to minimise interference with the south terrace.

or

One stair on the north side of the site, a bridge link across the canyon and one stair on the south side of the site, possibly a counter weighed stair to minimise interference with the south terrace.

A Home in the City

RENZO PIANO

I think that the dream of a 'family home', a personalised shelter, a space all for you and your family, is a fine and legitimate idea. But it has always been associated with living in the countryside, following a planning model based on suburban sprawl. I think that it is also worth, even necessary, taking a chance and imagining this same housing model in a densely built urban area. This means demonstrating that the desire for privacy, making a mark on one's own housing space, is not incompatible with the intensity of a metropolis.

It just has to be developed vertically.

As early as twenty years ago, together with Peter Rice and Ove Arup & Partners, we worked on this theme to define a duplex housing model, open to all flexible transformations: this project was called E.H. (Evolutive Housing).

The vertical aggregation of houses allows the gradual passage from the private to the public: from a place of intimacy (the first step of social aggregation), in other words the family, to the second, which is the landing on which twelve households, and so about thirty people, converge.

The landing is the place where they meet, where they take the lift. It gives access to services and (in a 'live and work' vision) to share work and communication areas.

We then move on to the third step, that of broader social life, which is the garden, at the foot of the towers, a place that brings together 300 families.

Finally, there is the entire district, with all the archetypal places of a city and urban life: streets, squares, markets, shops, tradesmen and services. From there, through an intricate fabric of streets, routes then lead towards the station and the underground, moving on to the final and largest stage, the city itself.

Naturally, one of the biggest problems is that vertical construction has always been associated with office blocks. And office blocks are often a semantically arrogant expression, hermetic, inexpressive, sometimes aggressive buildings.

But the idea of living in the clouds, seeking for a lighter, less predictable expression, is not a long shot. It means stratifying functions, accepting that the road level and the level connected to it are the urban level. They are the point of encounter with the rest of the city. While the higher levels are those of more private social life, right into the intimacy of one's own home.

This competition, as I understand it, aims to project a vision of lightness and transparency into the future of the city.

Renzo Piano

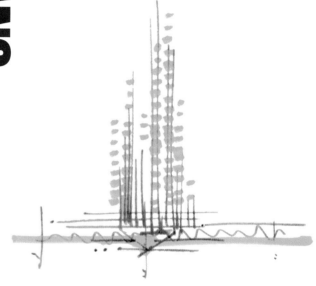

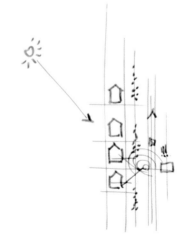

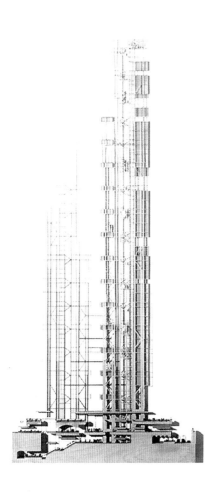

Tower section

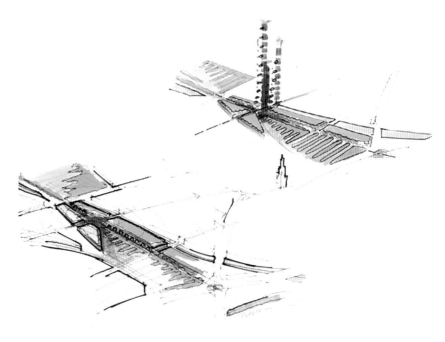

Urban strategy

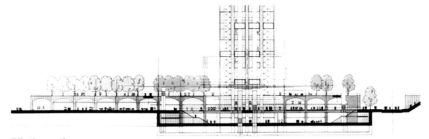

Plinth section

Plinth perspective

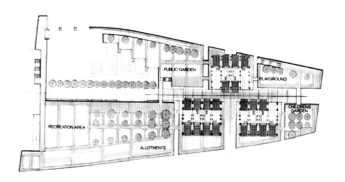

Garden level plan

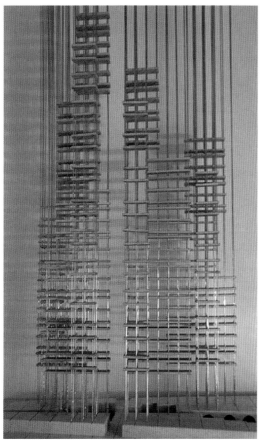

Study model

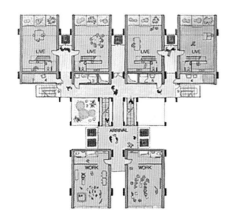

Work/live cluster plan

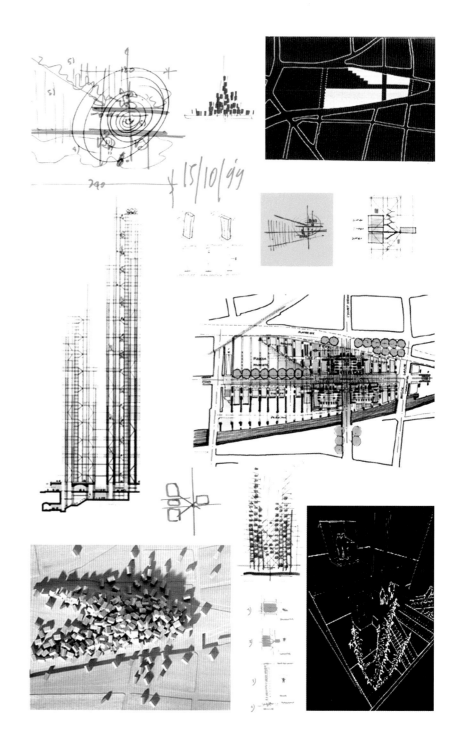

15/10/99

'House' elevation

Renzo Piano Building Workshop, architects
Design team: J. Moolhuijzen (architect in charge)
with B. Akkerhuis, J. Carter, K. van Casteren,
O. Hempel, A. Meier, M. Prini
and B. Payson, B. Vapné; Y. Kyrkos,
F. de Saint-Jouan (models)

Consultants: Ove Arup & Partners
(structural and environmental aspects);
Bob Lang (engineer in charge),
Barry Jefcoate, Jonathan Ward.

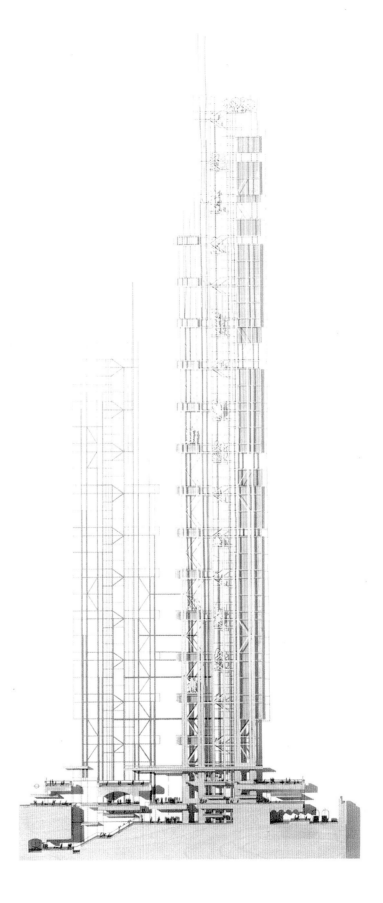

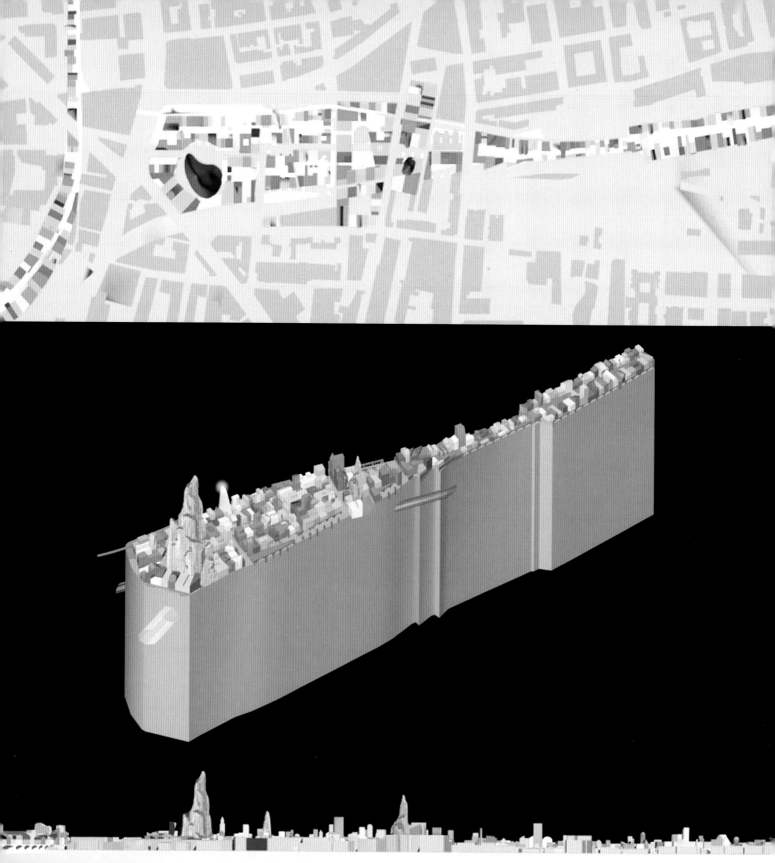

WEST 8

New Urban Landscape

Living in the City is a manifesto for new urban conditions for accommodating dwellings as an alternative to sprawl. This ambition fully benefits from the potential of derelict sites.

This entry for the Bishopsgate site investigates the combination of small scale, high density development, the archaeology of the existing site and the implantation of an artificial landscape.

Within the existing structure, an urban tissue will be achieved though precise excavation. The historic arches will absorb a highly diverse programme of shops, studios, community facilities and services. This excavated archaeology will respect and enhance the heritage of this magnificent site.

On top of the arches a colonisation process will start, based on a small-scale parcelation grid. The grid is derived from the existing structure, but at the same time allows for a myriad of possibilities. Once the number of new levels exceeds the threshold limit, the existing structure is reinforced, or removed to carry new structure and higher loads. At certain points, up to 10 levels can exist.

Individual landowners will develop their own lot, within a multi-coloured new identity, like a city within a city. Developers and citizens are offered a high degree of flexibility. Property can be accessed mainly from the ground level.

In this low rise/high density area three magnificent landscape features, the Peaks, will be raised. These rocks have an Arcadian presence and form micro biotopes. They will be icons of urban nature on the scale of London, and will be a novel construction challenge.

The derelict urban strips, of which the site forms a part, link the new city with London's larger bike network providing fast and efficient access and routes for the cyclists and pedestrians of London.

Acknowledgements:
WEST 8 / Landscape Architects and Urban Planners

Project Leader: Ronald Wall

Team: Adriaan Geuze, Edzo Bindels, Henk Hartzema, Helena Casanova, Theo Deutinger, Jesus Hernandez, Halina Mielnik, David Papapoulos, Riikka Tuomisto

Photography: Jeroen Musch

Consultants: Gregory Phillips Architects and ca+pe / Stephen Bundy

Model: Made by Mistake

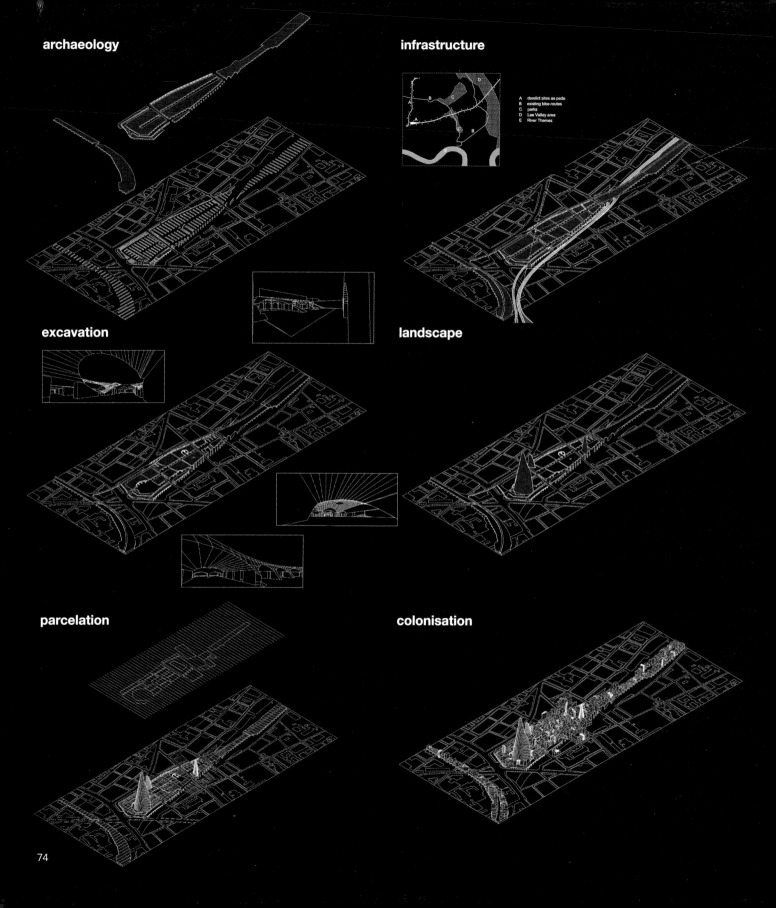

archaeology

infrastructure

A derelict sites as pede
B existing bike-routes
C parks
D Lee Valley area
E River Thames

excavation

landscape

parcelation

colonisation

74

West 8

archaeology

cave

excavation

house-patio

landscape/peaks

garden-patio

parcelation

100%

colonisation

tower

SUSTAINABLE CONSTRUCTION

Our sponsorship of Living in the City came about as a result of our conviction that design must create close alliances with industry. This initiative is one of a group of activities, supported by Corus, with the aim of encouraging and recognising excellence in design and sustainable solutions.

Our commitment to sustainable design means encouraging employees, suppliers and design teams to maintain sound environmental practices. We believe that sustainability is about protecting and enhancing the environment, while seeking to satisfy people's needs – in this case the need to reduce economic and social isolation by creating better communities for people living in our cities. It is our view that sustainability should encompass environmental, social and economic goals for a better quality of life for everyone now, and for future generations to come.

Our city centres have reached a watershed in terms of their need for change and the application of new ways of thinking. The way people live and the buildings they live in are at the heart of bringing about this change, and we hope that some of the ideas and solutions generated by Living in the City will act as a catalyst for developing new techniques in sustainable construction.

Geoff Hooker,
Corporate PR and Brand Director, Corus

corus

ALTERED PLACES

Continued from page 23

Difference is accelerated by segregation, and we know from history that separating diverse peoples or cultures into distinct areas can lead to the ghetto. If this is so at the scale of the city, then segregation at the scale of the street or the individual block may also be problematic. Separating social and private housing into distinct blocks reinforces their differences. Community groups and facilities can create an impression of organised local communities, but this is false as community centres are usually empty, infrequently attended, and few people even know their neighbours, let alone spend their social time with them. As individuals we actively practice social integration, and most people have relatives and friends who are richer and poorer than themselves. Our social networks are several, but dispersed rather than with our next door neighbour. The quality of our environment matters more, and being free from danger, noise and pollution is more central to our perceived quality of life than being on intimate terms with our neighbours.

Will new mixed developments prevent social exclusion, and can the socially diverse activities and roles of people richer and poorer be whipped up into a coherent and yet differentiated arrangement of homes and spaces? – Is it just a question of getting the ingredients in the right proportions? Like cooking, it is probably as much a matter of having the right, and fresh ingredients, and working with them with as light a touch as possible. It may be that rather than any specific proportion of the mix of mortgages and tenancies it is the environmental quality of the spaces in which they mix that is crucial. Social integration may not be amenable to a diagrammatic spatialisation, and it is unlikely that any particular order or mix of homes in blocks and streets will, by itself, produce social coherence. Well made and well connected places that have a carefully constructed spatial identity will allow may different kinds of people to live harmoniously next to each other, precisely because it will enable them to belong to and be active in several dispersed communities. The most critical task is the creation of urban spatial relations, the form and physical arrangements of shared and private.spaces that are fluidly connected to urban passages and transit spaces, and thus to the city as a whole.

The potential dichotomy between environmentally sustainable low density and economically sustainable high density may be resolved in another new architecture, developed from the reinvention of the high-rise tower. What is certain is that new kinds of domestic spaces are required, which must have the economic potential to be affordable for different parts of society. This will force a revision of current building practices, needing an inventive material and technical strategy that is closer to the patterns of industrial production. The live/work description of the kind of undivided spaces produced in the regeneration of old industrial buildings is not just the craft industry category given by some planners. Nor is it just a means for an aesthetic production of 'lofts' inhabited by the rich and the marginal. Live/work spaces are a response to an emerging need, indeed a preference for a flexible space that will allow for many different ways of living and working. It may be that this is the prototype of a new kind of living space. The emergence of systemic and demographic changes to our ways of life, the new patterns of movement and work demand flexible spaces, inventive homes and places that have the capacity to adapt in a future of uncertainty and flux.

Michael Weinstock
January 2000